MW01042019

THE RED DYES: COCHINEAL, MADDER, AND MUREX PURPLE

THE RED DYES: COCHINEAL, MADDER, AND MUREX PURPLE

A World Tour of Textile Techniques

Gösta Sandberg

Lark Books

Layout: Lena Nessle
Production: Elaine Thompson
Translation from the Swedish: Edith M. Matteson

Library of Congress Cataloging-in-Publication Data
Applied for

10 9 8 7 6 5 4 3 2 1

Copyright © 1994 by Gösta Sandberg
Original title: Purpur Koschenill Krapp
First published by Tidens förlag, Stockholm 1994
Published in agreement with Tidens förlag, Stockholm,
    represented by ICBS, Skindergade 3B, DK-1159 Copenhagen K.
English translation copyright ©1997 Lark Books

Published by Lark Books, 50 College Street, Asheville, NC 28801

English translation copyright ©1997 Lark Books

Distributed in the U.S. By Sterling Publishing,
    387 Park Ave. South, New York, NY 10016; 800/367-9692

Distributed in Canada by Sterling Publishing,
    c/o Canadian Manda Group, One Atlantic Ave.,
    Suite 105, Toronto, Ontario, Canada M6K 3E7

Every effort has been made to ensure that all the information in
this book is accurate. However, due to differing conditions, tools,
and individual skills, the publisher cannot be responsible for any
injuries, losses, or other damages that may result from the use
of the information in this book.

Printed in Hong Kong

ISBN 1-887374-17-5

To my children

Olle

Lasse

Kristina

Per

Jessica

Sofia

Daniel

Contents

Inga Wintzell

A Meeting With the Author

A meeting with Gösta Sandberg — if only from a distance by phone —
is a fascinating experience. Before you know it, you feel as if you have
been taken far away from everyday life, perhaps to Macedonia or
Indonesia. Or, perhaps, to some other place on earth where his love of
exploration and his singular ability to make human contact on all lev-
els produces triumphs with rich yields. Dedicated and unobtrusive at
the same time, he freely shares his memories from an endless supply
of experiences, impressions, and observations.

Nature's cycle and ecological interplay are of central importance
to his research, touching him emotionally and aesthetically. Yes, he
experiences the beauty of nature with all of his senses. But now and
then certain selected representatives from the plant and animal kingdoms particularly interest him on a more theoretical level: a
Mediterranean mollusk, or rather the secretion that comes from it, a
Mexican cactus and the insect that is nourished by it, and a less exotic
plant with root fibers that have the same qualities. These are the cre-
ations that play the leading role in this, his newest book. This book is
the 18th in a series on textile dyeing, a subject that has interested him

since his training period at *Slöjdföreningen*, the Handicraft Association's school in Göteborg, during the early 1950s. Although his original studies were in graphic art and decorative painting, his curiosity and sense of smell led him to the school's batik workshop, which had been spreading its waxy odors through the corridors for a long time.

That is how it started, a little unplanned and tentative. But Gösta Sandberg is a diligent person and soon he was involved with his studies in color and dyeing (both practical and theoretical) in labs, museums, and above all in nature, where the basic materials in their various guises were to be obtained. His first trip was to Java and it was closely followed by others; soon he had served his apprenticeship. He became a specialist, teaching chromatics and textile dyeing at the *Konstfackskolan*, the College of Arts, Crafts, and Design in Stockholm.

Those days are long gone. While he continues to spread his knowledge, now he does it from Nora, a picturesque, idyllic area in the mining district of Västmanland. That is where his home and his family, his library with volumes that range from the 1500s to recent reports, and his miscellaneous collection of colored textiles from near and far are located. In other words, it is a well-equipped research center for him and for special interest researchers from all over the world. Gösta is generous; he shares. He is also systematic and has an obvious talent for organization. An entire army of friends, volunteers, and enthusiastic co-workers within various disciplines are his supporters.

He has a kindred soul in Pliny the Elder, the Roman public official who wrote his scientific work *Historia Naturalis* around the time of the birth of Christ. Gösta Sandberg is well acquainted with these writings, from which so much of his information is derived. He translates, explains, and brings to life processes that are thousands of years old. For example, he tells myths of how the purple color from the mollusk on the beach became the finished dyestuff that was desired by luxury-thirsty sovereigns and mighty potentates. His stories are filled with tension and drama, strongly emphasizing the large and small contributions of private individuals in the multi-faceted history of dyeing over thousands of years.

The symbolism and tradition connected with blue and red, as well as what they meant culturally and economically, are what Gösta Sandberg has brought to us in two of his books, with himself as an intermediary. Fortunately, a great number of colors remain at his disposal. Which one will it be next time?

Author's Foreword

Three red colors will be described in this book, three colors that have been used for as long as mankind has been able to dye textile fibers. They have been derived from three of the four elements: the bluish-red purple color from mollusks in the great oceans of the world, the warm red madder color from root fibers found in limy fields, and finally the glowing scarlet color from a humble little insect. With the help of heat from a fourth element, their origins (from completely different starting materials) have been converted to shining red colors on textile products of various types.

Together with deep blue indigo, the three reds have become the most significant and indispensable dyes of all time. No other colors could even come close to filling the demand for fastness combined with great aesthetic qualities. No advanced culture in the East or the West has been without them in the textiles they created.

The chemical composition and use of blue dyestuff from indigo has long been known and well-documented. Despite prolonged research, though a series of unanswered questions remain regarding the red dyestuffs. For example, the series of steps used in the most complicated dye process known to man — the dyeing of Turkey red — has not yet been satisfactorily explained. A great deal of space has been devoted to this process and to the textile products that have been produced at various times, primarily Indian and Persian calico prints, and later the multicolored "Indians" from Mulhouse and Glarus, using this fascinating method. The text is supplemented with unique photos of designs, recipes, and excerpts of test samples as well as original prints from the centuries-old archival treasures of the manufacturers.

The magic-filled, strong red cochineal dye of the South American Indians, which was used long before the encroachment of the Europeans, is described in full detail. The same is true of several other equally interesting but seldom mentioned color scale insects, the Indian lac scale insect and the Armenian kermes scale insect. Dyestuff from the latter was used on Vasco da Gama's scarlet-red clothing and the cardinal-red *mozzetta* of Pope Paul II.

Dyeing with genuine purple, a mystery that is over 600 years old, is now about to be satisfactorily solved, and Pliny's descriptions on the subject in his *Historia Naturalis* are confirmed on several points. This dyeing method is described in the section about purple in this book, as well as the little known purple dyeing methods that were used for ages by Central American Indian tribes that lived on the coast of the Pacific Ocean. The less well-known methods from the 600s, in which the Irish and Nordic people captured and used the purple mollusks, are also described. One of the final sections of the book contains recipes and instructions for currently used methods of dyeing with madder and cochineal. In this section, thoughts about the environmental aspects of dyeing with natural dyestuffs are restated. The chemical composition and qualities of the dyestuffs described in the book should be of special value to people who are interested in textile science. Dyestuff analysis makes it possible to examine the older textiles in the photos, and the results are given in the captions.

There is a living individual behind each innovation and process in dye technology; not just a name, a date, and a place on the map. My intention is to bring these people and the conditions under which they worked to life. But, in order to be able to do this, I had to limit certain parts of my presentation. The abbreviated entries serve as coherent background for the parts of the book that received more detailed attention and serve my purpose.

I have also placed special emphasis on material of which I have personal knowledge because I traveled to the areas in question, held conversations with dyers and textile printers, or learned as a result of my own work in this field.

Gösta Sandberg
Nora/Rättvik 1994

Introduction

In the Presence of a Red Color . . .

Sometimes we experience moments that are unlike any other. I had such a moment one day many years ago as I stood near a red flag with the following text in golden Cyrillic print: "Freedom or death for the people of Krusevac." Beside me stood an old man who had been present the first time that red cloth was hung out on the balcony of the house where we now stood. The event had occurred on St. Elijah day in 1903, and the place was the little mountain town of Krusevac in Macedonia. With his defiant action he and his comrades wanted to mark the end of the 500-year Ottoman rule and offer hope for new times in freedom for their people. The incident, known as the Ilinden revolt in history books, was crushed after 30 bloody days; it would be several years before the word *Svoboda* in the flag's golden text would become reality.

Above: The red flag from the Ilinden revolt in 1903.

Below: The red felt piece from Macedonia.

Opposite page: Thoughts about a "chardak," Galicnik, Macedonia.

The reason I happened to be traveling in this remote and inaccessible mountain district was also related to a piece of red cloth: a coarse madder red and black bit of felt that was placed in my hand after a lecture in Slovenia's capital of Ljubljana. Niko Krajl, the brilliant designer of the folding chair, gave it to me. Accompanying the gift was an urgent request to visit Macedonia, where I would meet "a people who radiate with the same vitality and energy" as the redness of the piece of felt I held in my hand. I went, and was met everywhere by the kind of people that my friend Niko predicted I would meet: shepherds, dyers, and weavers who, despite great poverty and hard lives, let the double flutes play and the embroidery needle run over the surface of linen fabric.

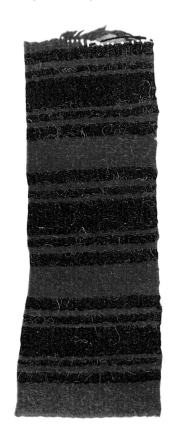

On the first trip I found something unlike anything I had ever encountered, something I realized would not be possible to find for long. Consequently, many more trips followed and, where the small plane or the worn jeep could not reach, the back of a horse carried me and the textile colleague who sometimes accompanied me. During these trips, which were taken with the help of grants from various scientific institutions, aging and rapidly disappearing weaving, embroidery, and dyeing techniques were photographed and documented.

The madder red color dominated in the textiles wherever we went: on the rich embroidery of the clothing, in the hand-made rugs, or in the coarse goat hair blankets that protected us against the night cold. Fortunate circumstances made it possible to discuss and analyze the collected materials with our hosts of many years, Slavka Zarceva and her sister, Maritza Popstefanieva. The latter is the author several classic works on Slavic embroidery techniques and the folk art of dyeing. My thoughts often rest at their house with the white staircase and the blue doors near the shores of Lake Ohrid.

If there are those who are expecting me to share thoughts about the influence of the color red on our psyche, or about the relationship between the soul of the Macedonian people and the color red, I will have to disappoint them. The question is totally uninteresting to me. An interplay of a more obvious nature is the influence of the limy fields on the content of the dyestuff from the madder roots and, thereby, the extreme chroma of the red threads that are used in the most famous of all embroidery techniques.

The strong and lasting feeling I experienced with the Macedonians was not tied to the red color as much as it was a deeply touching meeting with a wild but attractive landscape, with tough but good people, and to a singular but threatened folk textile art.

One late summer day I stood on the pier at the foot of Rättvik's church waiting for the church boats that approach with their oars raised in greeting. A little later the Dalecarlian men in long blue coats and the Dalecarlian women in red hoods and scarves walked up toward the church for the morning services.

The rowers of the church boat greet Rättvik's church by raising their oars.

As I sat in the last pew watching the congregation in their brightly colored costumes in front of me, I was struck, like so many times before, by the variety and distinctiveness of the red portions of the costumes. But this time I make an observation that I really should have made a long time ago. The pattern and colors on the scarves and hoods matched what I had seen worn by the festively clad participants at *Svadban*, the annual wedding festival in Galicnik, near the Macedonian-Albanian border.

The wonder that was awakened and the questions that I associated with these observations remained unanswered for several years. They answers were finally given to me in Glarnerland, the little Swiss Alp province from which one of the reddest of all calico prints once spread to practically the entire globe. My authority was the descendant of, and bore the same name as, those who nearly 300 years ago started the business, the traces of which I so strongly experienced in both Galicnik and Rättvik. Through their generosity I was finally able to add the last piece to the puzzle that this book about red textiles sometimes seems, to me, to represent.

On the road between Galicnik and Debar the 400-year-old Turkish bridge still spans its arch across the deep river ravine.

Purple

From the *Aeneid* by Virgil

The Fourth Book: Dido's Love and Death

On the first hutments, there he found Aeneas
Laying foundations for new towers and homes.
He noted well the swordhilt the man wore,
Adorned with yellow jasper; and the cloak
Aglow with Tyrian dye upon his shoulders—
Gifts of the wealthy queen, who had inwoven
Gold into the fabric.

Dawn came up meanwhile from the Ocean stream,
And in the early sunshine from the gates
Picked huntsmen issued: wide-meshed nets and snares,
Broad spearheads for big game, Massylian horsemen
Trooping with hounds in packs keen on the scent.
But Dido lingered in her hall, as Punic
Nobles waited, and her mettlesome hunter
Stood nearby, cavorting in gold and scarlet,
Champing his foam-flecked bridle. At long last
The queen appeared with courtiers in a crowd,
A short Sidonian cloak edged in embroidery
Caught about her, at her back a quiver
Sheathed in gold, her hair tied up in gold,
And a brooch of gold pinning her scarlet dress.

—(*The Aeneid*. Virgil. Translated by
Robert Fitzgerald. Random House, Toronto: 1983.)

A Color from the Kingdom
of the Blood Red Man

A Color as Precious as Gold, Silver, and Pearls

Throughout all time, and with all people, certain things have come to be valued more highly than others. Perhaps they were difficult to produce, had greater durability or longevity than corresponding items, or maybe their production was very limited. These factors made them desirable and gave them high status. A consequence of this has sometimes been that they have come to be considered bearers of high aesthetic value. There are few things cultivated by humans that meet this criteria better than the color purple.

Of the thousands of color names we know and encounter daily in various connections, nothing has the ring to it that the word purple does. No other color is as surrounded by myths, tales, and fleeting mystery. And are there any writers of antiquity who do not let purple illustrate the splendor and value of clothing, the triumphs of unlimited power, or the sweetness of a love encounter between gods or humans?

Three types of wool products, each dyed with a substance of animal origin, are counted among the most highly valued of antiquity's treasures — in a class with gold, silver, and pearls. One, the scarlet red color, was dyed with the lac scale insect kermes, while both of the others were dyed with material obtained from several types of mollusks: a bluish one called *purpura hyacinthina* and a more reddish one called *purpura blatta* or Tyrian purple.

The purple dyestuff, or more correctly the preliminary stage of the color, is produced in a gland of the so-called gastropod-mollusks, and even there we find different types of purple mollusks. The most well known of these is found in the Mediterranean, the Indian Ocean, and on the coast of the Pacific Ocean in South America. The dyestuff itself has since been derived from the secretion from the gland by subjecting it to a number of more or less complicated processes.

"Oh Tyre, you say yourself:
I am the fullness of beauty.
Dark blue and purple red cloth
from the island country of Elisa,
came your sun tent."

— The prophet Ezekiel

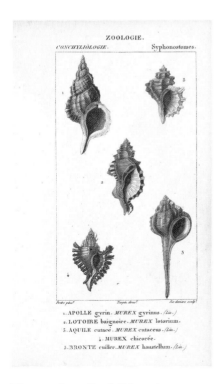

The purple mollusk (Murex).
Copperplate from the early 1800s.

19

Murex brandaris.

Phoenicia: The Kingdom of the Blood Red Men

In prehistoric times the production of purple was often associated with the Phoenician cities of Tyre and Sidon (now Saida), both of which were mentioned in Egyptian sources from the time of Thotmes III, one-and-a-half millennia before our chronology begins. Along with the colonial city of Carthage, they were considered the Phoenician kingdom's largest and most powerful cities.

An older name for Tyre was "Sarre" (Sur), which means that we find the expression Sarranus used by the writer Virgil about the color purple.

Phoenicia covered the coastal stretch between Anatolia in the north and Palestine in the south: that is, modern Lebanon and neighboring parts of Syria and Israel. Although the land of the Phoenicians was small, they controlled all the waterways in the Mediterranean. The inhabitants were known as skilled craftsmen and merchants as well as good colonizers, and their connections to India and other distant countries made them significant carriers of the impulses and knowledge of far-off cultures. But in one area they themselves became forerunners. With greater skill than others, and in a manner never before known, they dedicated themselves to the art of dyeing purple.

The Greek name of Phoenicia was *Phoinike,* formed from the word *phoinos,* blood red, which in time became an increasingly telling epithet about the land and its people. The crew of the Phoenician ship also went under the name "the blood red men," because their faces were always red from the winds of the seas, and because their clothing always included sections of purple.

Because a murex mollusk gives off only a few small drops of the sought-after secretion for dyeing with purple, millions of these mollusks were needed annually for production at the many dye works.

A study that illustrates this was done between 1906 and 1909 by the German chemist Paul Friedländer. He demonstrated that 12,000 *Murex (Bolinus) brandaris* mollusks could only produce .049 ounces (1.4 grams) of pure dyestuff. Consequently, an enormous number of mollusks had to be collected and processed to meet the increasing demand for purple-colored products, loose wool, yarn, and fabrics. There are still mile-long stretches of beach around the cities of Tyre and Sidon in Lebanon that are covered several yards thick by layers of smashed shells — an eloquent reminder of an industry that once brought both cities unparalleled riches.

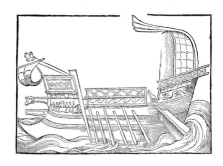

Vessel from Hellenic times.
From a work by Antonius Thylesius,
Venice, 1549.

20

"The holy purple mollusk must be worshiped."

— Theodosius the Great

The limited access to purple mollusks, the minimal quantity of the dye-producing secretion, and the degree of difficulty involved in the dyeing process made purple-colored products enormously expensive to produce. Naturally they became the most expensive of antiquity's goods, reserved for kings, emperors, and the upper classes of society. Only the highest public officials in Rome had the right to wear the status symbol Toga praetexta, a cloak with one or more purple edges in varying widths. The purple dyers formed their own fraternity within the dyers' guild, which was controlled by imperial public officials who scrupulously supervised the lucrative state monopoly. The significance of the color purple in the Roman Empire is perhaps made most evident from a passage in Theodosius the Great's statute book from the fifth century B.C., where he declares that "the holy purple mollusk must be worshiped - *Murex sacerado randus.*"

The Old Testament offers numerous examples of purple's use as a status symbol. The adjacent quote comes from the original Hebrew text, and differs from modern languages on a point that is important to this book. A clear distinction is made between blue purple *(tekhelet)* and red purple *(argaman)* in the description of the various articles of clothing in Mordecai's costume.

When Alexander the Great conquered the city of Shushan during the campaign against the Persians in the year 331 B.C., he found no fewer than 5,000 *"talents"* (a *talent* = 55 pounds/25 kilograms) of purple-colored material from the Greek city of Hermione among the royal treasures. They had been stored on the shelves in the treasury room for nearly 200 years, and they still had their original fresh and strong color. It is told that this part of the war booty was especially valued by the emperor.

בִּדְבַר הַמֶּלֶךְ וְדָתוֹ נִתְּנָה בְּשׁוּשַׁן הַבִּירָה׃ ‏15
מִלִּפְנֵי הַמֶּלֶךְ בִּלְבוּשׁ מַלְכוּת תְּכֵלֶת וָחוּר וַעֲטֶרֶת
וְתַכְרִיךְ בּוּץ וְאַרְגָּמָן וְהָעִיר שׁוּשָׁן צָהֲלָה וְשָׂמֵחָה
הָיְתָה אוֹרָה וְשִׂמְחָה וְשָׂשֹׂן וִיקָר׃ ‏17וּבְכָל־מְדִינָה וּ

"When Mordecai left the king in royal garments of blue purple and damask and with a large golden crown, and with a cloak of red purple, the city of Shushan rejoiced and was glad."

— Esther IIX: 15

Alexander the Great; coin from Macedonia.

A Color for Gods, Emperors, and Courtesans

The Roman kingdom was strongly divided by class, and one's clothing revealed one's class. For nearly a millennium the greatest plague of the free Romans was the so-called toga, which was worn completely plain and in the original yellowish-white color of the wool. The emperor and the most highly ranked public officials, on the other hand, wore expensive purple-colored togas with gold embroidery. Low-ranking public officials could only wear what was called a purple edge, that is a purple-colored band along one edge of the toga. The clergymen of the various gods were also entitled to use the purple color for their clothing. As their everyday clothing, both men and women wore short-sleeved white tunics. On festive occasions these tunics were exchanged for a variation with broad purple edges that extended from their shoulders down to their ankles.

We gladly consider the simplicity of the Roman costume, with a combination of only white, purple, and gold, austere and aesthetically pleasing. In Greek Sparta, though, this combination was regarded as far too colorful and provocative. The Draconian, uncompromising Spartans considered dyeing textile materials "deceiving nature." The Greek word *dolon* means both to dye and to deceive. Consistent with this, the Spartans banished the first dyers from their city.

Eventually, the Spartans gave up that strict viewpoint regarding dyed goods, allowing their war crews, for example, to wear red-colored clothing. The red color gradually came to play an increasingly important role in Greek dress customs, but was not regulated with the same strictness as it was later in Rome.

For centuries the Phoenicians kept purple production methods secret. When the Greeks finally got that knowledge from them and discovered purple mollusks on the banks of their own coasts, they began to take over a large part of the Phoenician's production and trade of this expensive ware.

In Hermon, the original home of the Greek-Dorian culture, there were purple dye works with highly developed production techniques. It was here that Alexander the Great's formerly discussed war booty of purple dyed cloths had been produced, and the Persian court requisitioned its purple cloths from here as well.

Purple dye works were found on Crete and Corinth early on, and their significance is eloquently testified to by the fact that the purple mollusk was depicted on their coins.

While the design of clothing and the role of purple in this connection was strictly regulated in Rome, the status of the Greek costume seems a bit blurry.

The costume of the Athenian was discrete and elegant at the same time, most often undyed wool or flax with only a few colored edges on the lower edge of the gown. Further back, they had used imported Oriental flower patterned cloths. These were later reserved for adorning images of gods and in connection with the theater. In order to persuade the "Arabian women" to refrain from using these flowered — but probably popular — materials, they resorted to laws that reserved them for flute players and prostitutes of various ranks. The latter had previously been given the right to walk the streets bare breasted, with their hair hanging down, and to use cloth so thin that nothing could be hidden underneath. One regulation that they had to follow was that their hair had to be golden yellow, dyed with saffron.

Eventually the prostitutes began to appear in purple and gold knitted clothing. In light of this, it was found necessary to institute a series of clothing and luxury ordinances so they did not irritate the free but poor population by outshining them with their outer splendor. Compliance with these dubious ordinances was complicated by the fact they were not uniformly enforced. In Syracuse, and above all in Sparta, clothing made from expensive purple materials and gold was entirely reserved for prostitutes, and the prohibition was applied to "the Arabian women" instead.

The entry of courtesans on the scene became an additional irrational factor that the bureaucrats had not counted on when they wrote their ordinances. This group of women was primarily unbound by the bonds of family life and spent time with men under less stringent circumstances, participating in their literary and philosophical social gatherings. The most famous of them was Aspasia, who lived with the politician Pericles, whom she eventually married. Through her beauty and refined manners she came to play a significant role in the circle of cultural personalities that gathered in his home.

Some very esteemed courtesans lived like queens and chose clothing and colors accordingly. No legal measures against them could come into question, despite their disrespectful undermining of the prohibitive regulations. They lived with, and were protected by, society's leading classes, and in this connection the laws were just as transparent as the courtesan's hyacinth-colored clothing.

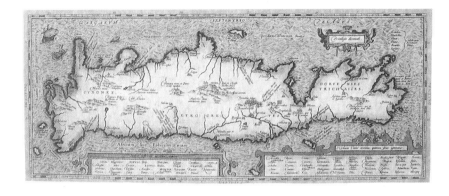

Map of Crete, 1584.

Purple in the World of Myths and Legends

Hercules Discovers Purple

In Greek mythology the word purple is mentioned in numerous places. One myth describes how this singular color was discovered. During the romantic encounter of Hercules and the nymph Tyros, the mythical hero's dog crushed and ate the contents of some purple mollusks that were thrown up on the beach by the waves. Afterward, the dog's nose turned a deep reddish color that had never been seen before. Tyros now informed Hercules that if he could get her a garment in that beautiful color, he could expect more pleasant hours together with her. Hercules did not waste time; he immediately collected a large number of mollusks from which he produced a brew that he used to dye the desired garment for his beloved.

In a famous sketch in oil, the Flemish painter Peter Paul Rubens has depicted this old legend of Hercules discovering purple. With all due respect and admiration for the description in Greek mythology, it must be admitted that this story contains quite a bit of fantasy in terms of dyeing technology. The apocryphal literature of the Old Testament, on the other hand, contains a variation of events that possesses a greater measure of technical probability. (See page 188.)

Fragment of a tunic from Palmyra, Syria. Part of the front and arm, in plain woven linen with tapestry decor of wool dyed with mollusk purple. From the second century A.D.

The Shepherd and the Color Purple

Hiram was the king of Tyre, and this took place during his time. A dog that was running along the beach found a mollusk that had been thrown up by the waves. When he bit it, his nose was covered with the blood of the mollusk. A shepherd who saw this got a little bit of wool and used it to dry off the dog's nose. From the wool, he braided a band and put it on his head. When he walked around in the sun after that everybody who saw him thought that they saw glowing rays coming from his head. When Hiram heard about this he sent for the shepherd and the sight of the red wool amazed him. When all the dyers got together they, too, were amazed by what they saw. Then they each went their own way to investigate the matter and found similar mollusks, which greatly delighted them.

"When I was Young the Violet Purple Color was the Most Popular"

Despite the word purple being found in ancient sources over a long period of time, we seldom find any indication of how the color was produced. In other words, we find the word purple, but never anything about the dyestuff purple. However, considering the evidence that shows how expensive the product was, we have an inkling that its preparation was more complicated than the Greek myth about Hercules and Tyre leads us to believe. If we go a little further forward in history and stop at a time about 2,000 years from our own, we meet the first, and for a long time the only, work that describes purple from a variety of aspects — technical, cultural, historical, aesthetic, etc. The author was a Roman public official with a burning interest in practically every bit of knowledge available in his time. His name was Gaius Plinius Secundus (Pliny the Elder), and his work is still preserved in the impressive 37 volumes of his encyclopedia-like work *Historia Naturalis.*

Some sections that are of interest to this book have been extracted from book nine, and we can follow Pliny's own text, supplemented with clarifying additions and inserted commentary with occasional abbreviations.

About the Origin, Use, and Appearance of Purple in Rome

". . . I can bring to you the knowledge that the use of purple in Rome comes from the oldest times, but that Romulus only used it for his cloak and it is fairly certain that the first king to use a purple edged cloak and broader purple edges was Tullus Hostilius, after the victory over the Etruscans.

"Cornelius Nepos, who died during the government of the long-grieved Augustus, says: 'When I was young the violet purple color was the most popular and a pound of it cost 100 Dinars, and not long afterward the red purple came from Taranto (in Alpuia). Finally the double-dyed Tyrian purple arrived, which could not even be had for 1,000 dinars per pound. This was used the first time in a cloak with a band, but people were offended when Publius Lentulus Sprinther wore that cloak. But who doesn't use the same purple color today for covering cushions for the benches at the dinner table?'"

It is interesting that Pliny can so precisely account for how the mythical Romulus, one of the founders of Rome, used purple in the year 753 B.C. This quote from the North Italian author Cornelius Nepos throws light on the question of how purple actually looked, and shows that the word purple was not just an unambiguous concept but that the color tone could vary according to desire, from pure red to violet. The expensive double-dyed Tyrian purple, of which Nepos speaks, was regarded by Pliny as a luxurious exaggeration; there was an explanation of its possible origin. He believes that the process was a result of a dyer's intentional attempt to correct unsuccessful dyeing by dyeing over the original, thereby producing a "deeper and more refined appearance."

The method of creating new color nuances in this manner was not unknown to the dyers of the time. Pliny discusses how, for example, it was possible to treat loose wool, which was first dyed scarlet-red with kermes *(coccum),* in a new bath with "Tyrian purple" in order to get the so-called "hysgine" color.

In other places in the text he mentions the possibility of mixing dyestuffs from various types of purple mollusks to combine the high chroma of one with the superior fastness of another.

Modern researchers have demonstrated that it is entirely possible to produce completely different color tones from one and the same mollusk dyestuff. With secretions from the banded murex *(Murex trunculus)* it is possible to produce deep red, blue violet, and dark blue tones, depending on the technique. Many mysteries associated with antique purple dyeing, including some difficult-to-decipher passages in Pliny's text, may as yet be explained.

Murex trunculus.

About the Occurrence, Capture, and Dyeing of Purple Mollusks

The various types of purple that Pliny mentions are not always easy to identify and name using the terms of the day. This task is made more difficult by the fact that at least two murex mollusks that existed during his time were apparently eradicated by the Phoenicians due to over-harvesting. In the ninth book, chapters 33-35, Pliny describes a couple of mollusks that we recognize and believe we are able to name.

". . . *Bucinum minor* is a smaller shellfish which resembles the mollusk that gives a trumpet-like sound from a round mouth cut into the corner of the shell, therefore the Latin name *bucina* or trumpet. This mollusk lives by, and can only be collected around, skerries and steep cliffs. The other is called *purpura* and has a pipe-shaped spout through which the mollusk can stick out its tongue. In addition, it has spikes on its shell, which are not found on *bucinum minor*. But both shells have the same number of rings as their age in years."

Purpura haemastoma.

Commentary

Based on Pliny's description of "purpura," it is possible, with great probability, to assume that he meant the mollusk that we call the spiny dye murex (*Murex brandaris* or *Bolinus brandaris*) that exclusively gives a red color. The appearance and the conditions under which the other mollusk lives agrees quite well with the cliff mollusk (*Purpura haemastoma* or *Thais h.*) which only produces a red-purple color.

The mollusk used in dyeing over the kermes-dyed loose wool was undoubtedly the same purple mollusk, the secretion of which, through appropriate manipulation, could produce either a red or a blue color. In other words, it was the banded murex (*Murex trunculus*) that produced a color that Pliny called "Hysgine," but which we today call hyacinth purple.

Pliny also describes a number of mollusks of varying suitability for purple dyeing: the sediment-, seaweed-, and pebble-purple mollusks. These primarily distinguish themselves by feeding on the bottom on which they live.

About Capturing Purple Mollusks

The purple mollusk outside the coasts of Europe, Asia Minor, and North Africa were collected by fishermen who brought willow baskets weighted down with stones. They dropped the baskets down to the mollusk banks on the bottom of the sea, where they gathered a selection of older and stronger specimens and hoisted them up to the surface. Pliny tells of another manner of collecting the mollusks: a sort of small, fine-meshed lobster pot was put out where the water was deep. The pots were baited with so-called heart mussels; when the mollusks stuck the sharp tips of their tongues into the half-open mussel, the mussel immediately closed its shell and "the purple mollusk hangs there and because of its greediness can be lifted up out of the water. . ."

Regarding the most appropriate time for collection he says: ". . . It is best to capture them after the Dog Star goes up," that is, when Sirius rises over the horizon, "because then they hide in the sediment at the bottom. But the dye workshops don't know that, even though it is of the greatest importance. . "

The storms of winter made it impossible to collect the purple mollusk then, so it can be done only in the beginning of the fall and early in the spring. At that time the Mediterranean lies calm and the mollusk fishermen can, despite good camouflage color and pattern design on the purple mollusks, see them where they are lying in the open and are easy to watch on the bottom.

Dyeing with Purple Mollusks

The so-called purple gland containing the grayish-yellow secretion that is the preliminary stage for the coveted dyestuff is located in the "cloak" inside the mollusk's rectum. Using special tools — some have been preserved — the snail itself was removed, then the gland was cut and sprinkled with salt. Smaller specimens were crushed and salted in their entirety in the subsequent phases of the dyeing process. For reasons that are easily explained, there is some uncertainty regarding the details of the extraction and dyeing process. Handling had to be adjusted according to the secretion that could be obtained from the mollusk and the color it would produce. Within certain limitations, it was possible for the purple dyer to achieve results that were somewhere between what was required and what was desired. With the *Murex trunculus* mollusk the dyer could produce either a blue or red-purple color. Through subsequent treatment in baths containing iron salt and tanning material, the dyer could also turn the original red-purple color into various warm-brownish to brownish-black colors. Pliny mentions this, but does not describe it in more detail. The uncertainty that still reigns regarding the many phases of the dyeing process and their outcome have resulted in the dyeing process being called one of antiquity's greatest industrial secrets.

Scientists have recently studied and attempted to clarify this long-forgotten process. They have been successful in dyeing wool with purple secretion from crushed murex mollusks by following the instructions that Pliny gave, using only the materials and techniques that were accessible to the dyers of antiquity.

Pliny's instructions for the "Tyrian process" are reproduced here in somewhat abbreviated form, with emphasis on volume instructions translated to our system of measurements.

". . . After capture, the vein (gland) we spoke of earlier is removed. About .9 of a quart (1 l) of salt needs to be added to this for every 220 pounds (100 kg) of purple glands. Three days is a sufficient time to allow it to stand and draw. The fresher the salt the more powerful it is. . . 44 pounds (25 kg) of salt added to purple glands is added to 7.8 gallons (30 l) of water, heated up in a lead vessel, and kept at an even and moderate temperature with the help of pipes from an oven a little ways away. This makes the meat (muscle tissue) that necessarily accompanies the purple glands separate itself. After nine days the contents are strained in a kettle. A bit of loose wool that has been washed clean is dipped to test the color bath and the liquid is heated up until the results are certain. The wool is allowed to remain in the bath for five hours, then it is taken out and carded, and dipped down again until it has soaked up all the dyestuff. . ."

About Pliny

Many of us have encountered a citation or a reference to Gaius Plinius Secundus (Pliny the Elder) at some time or another. His publications provide modern scientists, researchers, and archaeologists with a bottomless resource for their work. The section about purple in this book would have been significantly poorer if we had not had access to his multi-faceted description in *Historia Naturalis*, which has rightfully been called "A comprehensive work, as diversified as nature itself."

Technical literature is of special value when the facts presented are experienced first hand. Pliny's description of the "Tyrian process," given above, was the result of his personal observations at a purple dye works near the coast of Judea. Its incompleteness and omissions seem insignificant compared to his otherwise relevant picture of the process. More often than not, technical literature presents what the author witnessed first hand, but the author may not have been able to draw expert conclusions. We can say of Pliny that he was very anxious to become familiar with his research, and this ambition would eventually cost him his life when Vesuvius erupted in the year 79 A.D.

In an eyewitness account by Pliny the Younger (Pliny's nephew) we can follow the dramatic sequence of events up to their tragic conclusion. The information and direct quotations come from Axel Mattson's book about Pliny the Younger's letters.

Pliny found himself at the Misenum naval base near Vesuvius the day before the volcano erupted, when he observed a large black cloud that arose from the volcano. He ordered that a ship immediately be prepared for departure so he could study the cause at close range. At the same time, he found out that the lives of a large number of people at the bottom of the volcano were in obvious danger. Glowing lava streamed down the slopes and an agitated lake placed them in an increasingly precarious situation. Then Pliny changed his original plan — to study the eruption — and boarded a ship himself, with the goal of saving those in distress.

"Ashes already fell on the ship, hotter and more dense the closer they got. Soon, pumice and stones that were coal black, burned by the fire, and broken apart fell on them as well. The ship could vibrate without warning, and the beaches became inaccessible because of the landslide from the mountain. For a moment he considered turning around, but he called to the steersman who rowed him toward it, "Fortune favors the brave. Set course toward Pompeii."

On the other side of the bay, Pliny attempted to calm the excited people by showing great indifference and pretended cheerfulness. Pliny took a bath and ate a meal while ash rain and stones fell on the house where he was staying. Flames from the volcano were visible the entire time, and massive, powerful tremors caused fields and buildings to rock. After having been in that vulnerable situation for two days, it was decided to return to the beach with the ship and try to get rescued. Surrounded by smoke and sulphur steam, they were separated. On the

Pliny's death when Vesuvius erupted in 79 A.D. Copper plate engraving from Historia Naturalis, *Paris, 1779.*

morning of the third day Pliny's dead body was discovered, wrapped in his cape and appearing to be sleeping. Courage and eagerness to learn characterized his life."

The End of Antique Purple

Before 1000 B.C., the Phoenicians produced and traded purple fabric. "The blood red men" from Tyre and Sidon freighted the coveted product to the far off Middle East and to all parts of the Mediterranean in the galleys of their ships.

Heaps of crushed mollusk shells on the Greek islands and along the Levantine coasts tell of long-term production of nearly unheard of dimensions. Recent archeological discoveries have been made in Lebanon of pieces of pottery from the 13th century B.C., with purple coatings on the inside. At other excavations, purple costumes and parts of costumes were found. They were particularly abundant in the Syrian city of Palmyra, also called the Queen of the Desert, which was destroyed in 273 B.C. It was possible on one approximately 1,700-year-old fragment to identify the color as genuine hyacinthine purple, that is bluish purple.

Some of the natural dyestuffs that have been in continuous use since the oldest times are still used, although on a smaller scale and for special purposes. Indigo, cochineal, and madder are examples. On the other hand, the era of antique purple dyeing is definitely over. Its end is closely connected to the fall of the Roman Empire and its division into eastern and western Roman empires. The former, with its capital of Byzantium (later Constantinople), sought to carry on the purple traditions; its emperor even signed his documents with a purple ink produced for his use alone.

In the beginning of the 600s, the East Roman Empire forced its way in and conquered Syria, Persia, and Egypt. In 638 the old purple city of Tyre fell into their hands, and in one fell swoop the production of purple basically collapsed. Since that time, several of the most important steps in the production process have been completely lost.

The Saracen's destruction of Tyre in 1291 was another hard blow to the weakened purple industry but it wasn't until 1453, when the Turks conquered Constantinople — and brought about the fall of the Byzantine Empire — that production completely ended. The word purple has lived on as a magical and valued color name.

The destruction of the cities of Tyre and Sidon in 1291.

Purple Outside the Mediterranean Region

Purple in Northern Europe and Central America

We have now discussed the purple color as it was developed and used in the Mediterranean region. Despite deficiencies in our knowledge, and a number of still unsolved puzzles, we are somewhat familiar with the history of purple. However, the same cannot be said about the treatment of purple in other parts of the world. Thus we are usually unaware that a purple mollusk, *Nucella lapillus*, was long used in northwestern Europe in the production of the coveted dyestuff. As early as the 700s, an English document describes the use of purple, primarily for marking various types of linens. In the Netherlands and in Norway this practice survived into the last century. There was still a small purple industry in Ireland in the 1600s, and in 1685 the British doctor, William Cole, did what may have been the first chemical tests on purple dyestuff.

The Nordic *Nucell* mollusk lives on the rocky beaches of the Swedish and Norwegian west coasts, but can be found in deeper waters right down to the Oresund. Its appearance can vary greatly in both shape and size. If we go outside the coasts of the Mediterranean and the North Sea, we also find marine life areas with mollusks that produce purple dyes. *Purpura persicaria* lives in the Indian Ocean and another type, *Purpura patula*, lives on the coast of Nicaragua.

In the same way that the treatment of purple was described earlier in the words of the historiographer Pliny, the existence and use of purple in northern Europe and Central America will be described below in the words of several other authors. Their less-well-known works, which we will quote from, are not from epochs as far distant as that of Pliny, but are interesting because they describe capture and dyeing methods that are completely different from those he mentions.

Nucella lapillus.

Murex haustellum.

The Purple Red Embroidery of the British and Irish

In a work published in London in 1778, *Historia Naturalis Testaceorum Britanniae*, a small section is devoted to purple mollusks that exist on the British coasts. The author, Emmanuel Mendes da Costa, was a member of a number of scientific institutions, including one in Florence, and his description of the occurrence and use of the Nucella mollusk deserves to be quoted.

"The mollusks are, when they are collected from the sea, usually covered with sediment, but after they are cleaned they make a beautiful sight. They appear in great numbers, mainly along the coasts of Great Britain and Ireland. This type gives a purple juice analogous with the Tyrian purple of antiquity. Mr. Cole gave the following account in Phil. Trans. in 1684: "There is a white gland that lies crosswise in a small groove closest to the head of the animal which must be dug out with the sharp point of a horsehair paintbrush. The letters, small areas that are to be dyed, show up as light green colors at first. If placed in the sun, the color changes in the following manner: first it turns deep green, then completely sea green, then a pale blue, next a purplish red, and finally a very deep, purplish red tone, after which the sun does not produce any further changes. But the final and most beautiful color is obtained by then washing the dyed object in boiling hot water and soap and drying it in the sun, producing a bright crimson-red color which is durable even though it does not need any "stryptic" to bond with."

Commentary

The text contains several interesting sections. It clearly describes all color changes that occur until the purple dyestuff is finished forming from the gland secretion, and indicates that sunlight is necessary for the purple to "be called forth." It is clear that the untreated secretion was directly used for dyeing or, as in this case, to measure with. The purple pre-stage remains water soluble until it is subject to sunlight, which makes it possible to dye in this manner.

The word "stryptic," which appears at the end of the text, can be translated as alum and thus there can be no doubt that it is used here in the sense of a mordant. We find it mentioned by the Greek historian Herodotos, who tells that Egypt's Pharaoh Amasis gave 1,000 "talents" of "strypteria," that is 26 tons of alum, for the rebuilding of the Apollo Temple in Delphi, which burned down in 548 B.C. There it was to be used as impregnation for timber.

Finally, the text emphasizes the meaning of what dyers' circles call "soaping" to achieve the greatest possible clarity and chroma of a dyed product. In continuing his account, Cole tells how, after the discovery of America, the cochineal dyestuff displaced the use of what, in his opinion, were more precious purple dyes, which are only used today for monograms on linens and similar things. However, he is convinced that his forefathers in an earlier era used the domestic purple mollusks in the same manner as Tyrian purple. He refers to both Bede Venerabilis, who was his source for some of the larger sections, and he quotes from Venerabilis' *Historia ecclestica gentis anglorum*, which was published in 731.

"There are great quantities of snails, from which a scarlet or crimson colored dyestuff can be extracted, the sought after redness of which never grows pale but becomes finer with age."

Commentary

Based on Cole's text, it is possible to conclude that, in olden times, the coastal inhabitants of Britain and Ireland used the purple color in the same manner as the Tyrian color was once used, that is for dyeing wool, yarn, and woven fabrics.

St. Bede, whose first name was Venerabilis (the one who is worthy of respect), was a prominent and learned theologian who was even called the "father of British historical research." He was born in Northumberland in 674 and died in 735.

The Purplish Red Skirts in Tehuantepec

Long before the arrival of the Europeans to Central America, the population used the red dyestuff of the sea mollusks for their textiles. Even a few years into this century, young women could be seen in the marketplaces of the city of Tehuantepec wearing purple skirts. They were called *de caracolillo* from *caracol,* meaning snail or mollusk in Spanish. They consisted of two straight lengths of cloth joined by a seam in yellow or orange yarn and finished with a deep pleat on one side. The relative rarity of the purple mollusk and the large numbers that would be needed to dye a certain amount of yarn, as well as the time and patience required for dyeing, made the *caracolillo* skirts costly and, eventually, increasingly difficult to acquire. In a report for *Anthropological Essays* (1909) Zelia Nuttall writes about her study of a surviving form of dyeing with the purple mollusk that has survived on the Pacific coast of Mexico.

The ancient Mexican method of dyeing using the preliminary stage of the dyestuff — without needing to kill the animal itself — has lived into our times in some areas. The picture from Mexico shows a newly colored skein of yarn that changes color tone from green to red-violet (purple) under sunlight.

"When spring comes, around the beginning of March, the fishermen go off in their boats that are loaded with skeins of cotton and travel north along the coast to seek certain cliffs that were left to dry when the tide water receded. A fisherman pries one mollusk after another loose from the wet cliffs and blows on it so that it excretes the pre-stage of the dyestuff, which resembles a milky scum. He lets one of the skeins of yarn slide across his wrist and draws the cotton thread through the scum of several mollusks until it is completely saturated. After each mollusk has secreted a small supply of the liquid dyestuff, the fisherman usually presses it against the cliff and waits until it attaches itself there; other fishermen leave the mollusks in a pool of water. When they have been treated in this manner, the same mollusk can give another, although smaller, portion of the dyestuff when the same cliff is visited on the way back. However, the Caracol mollusk has now become so rare that the fishermen are often forced to continue as far north as Huatsco, or even Acapulco, to fill orders for dyed cotton yarn. When the cotton thread is moistened with the color secretion it first turns green. Then, when it is dried by the rays of the sun, the green turns purple and becomes permanent. The dye only fades an insignificant amount after repeated washing and becomes an attractive and refined shade of violet.

"One thing that makes the dye annoying is the strong fishy smell that seems to be just as permanent as the color itself. This property might explain why Tyrian purple ceased to be used, and why Roman emperors and all those who wore purple clothing during classical antiquity made excessive use of perfumes."

Commentary

What is striking is that it is cotton that is being dyed, a condition similar to the one described by Mendes da Costa from England and Ireland. Pliny's description deals exclusively with wool and the same is true for the small fiber fragments that were found in the archeological excavations near the city of Sidon.

It is also interesting that the dyeing takes place in the dyestuff pre-stage, and not with any form of vat operation. The animal is not killed with this method and therefore, hopefully, avoids eradication. The statement that the unpleasant smell of the purple dyestuffs might have brought an end to purple dyeing is plausible, but in the best case is only a half-truth. Other causes, including the appearance of the color scale insect on the scene, were probably of equal importance.

In 1748 an historical account of trips to Central America written by the Spanish Ulloa brothers was published in Madrid. Their account creates a more complete picture of the Mexican purple extraction process.

"In Nicoya this mollusk is used to dye cotton thread, which is then used for ties and finer sewing work.

"Various methods of extracting the dyeing liquid are used. A number sacrifice the life of the animal. They extract it from the mollusk by laying it on its back in one hand while pressing it so hard with a knife that the color is squeezed out of the rear projection from the end where its head is located. The rear projection is then cut off and the body is thrown away. After having handled a large number of mollusks and collecting the dyestuff liquid in a vessel, the cotton yarn is pulled through it. . .

"Others extract the dye liquid by squeezing the animal without killing it. They do not completely remove it from the shell, but rather squeeze it so that it gives off its juice. Then they put the mollusk back on the cliff where they found it and it recovers and can then excrete more liquid after a short time, but not as much as the first time. If you repeat the procedure three or four times, you get very little the last time, and the animal can die from fatigue."

The 1744 account by the Ulloa brothers makes it clear that they witnessed the extraction method where the purple snail is killed; but they do not add that even in areas where the Indians used to collect these mollusks, the mollusks were found in large numbers and the method was usually not used. Because a large number of mollusks could only give a minimum of dye, they realized that the risk was too great for an intensive collection. Using the second and more merciful method made it possible for the mollusk to survive. The account also relates the odd belief (that was widespread in this area) that cotton yarn varied in weight and color depending on what time of day it was dyed.

35

Purple Imitations and Recipes

When the sultan Mehmet II placed a half moon on the dome of Hagia Sophia Basilica in Constantinople in May of 1453, it not only marked the fall of the Roman Empire, it also marked the end of antiquity's thousands of years of use of mollusk purple. When, after three days of excesses, the sultan made his entry into the conquered city, vast treasures had been removed, blood had flowed, and the last purple dye works was destroyed. At the same time, the collective imperial knowledge of the treatment of purple was turned to nothing.

The technical dyeing knowledge from more recent times, in the form of recipes and instructions, is preserved in richly detailed and exhaustive handbooks. But when researchers became interested in purple dyeing some decades ago, they came upon a technical vacuum. Only when the biological and chemical nature of the mollusk's dyestuff was clarified, experiments done on purple dyestuff discovered by archaeologists, and Pliny's somewhat brief instructions were translated, did we even come close to solving what has been called the 600-year-old mystery.

In this connection, it is usually pointed out that we still have a nearly 2,000-year-old collection of recipes with a number of descriptions of various procedures for the production of purple. What is being referred to here are the two handwritten papyrus manuscripts, *Papyrus Leiden* and *Papyrus Graecus Holmiensis* (probably parts of the same document), found at a grave site that was excavated near Thebes in Egypt in the year 1828. They are written by an unknown author and dated to the second century A.D. However, opinions about the value of the documents are strongly divided. Some regard them as "extremely valuable documents," while others, including the Englishman Pfister, believe they are evidence of a lack of technical knowledge and that the majority of the recipes have never been of great significance.

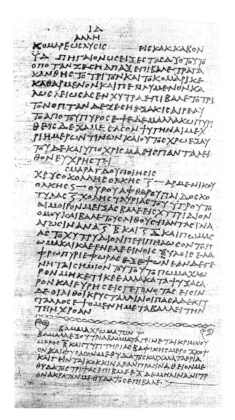

A page from Papyrus Graecus Holmiensis *(Royal Library Stockholm).*

While the instructions for dyeing wool contain a number of observations that hold up technically, it is possible to determine that they are both without substance and weakly formulated as far as the purple recipes are concerned. What is most surprising about the purple recipes is that none of them contains genuine purple secretion, despite columns entitled "Dyeing of Genuine Purple" or "Production of Tyrian Purple." Instead, there are dyestuffs like alkanet, orchil, and kermes, alone or in connection with woad. What is worth noting is that the word purple, when the collection of recipes was written, had become a visual quality as much as, or perhaps more than, a technical term.

I myself am also doubtful that the Papyrus manuscripts could have made up a collection of recipes in the current sense of the word, and the reasons are many. No dyer in older times would have used any written recipes or instructions.

Even the most skilled dyers were illiterate and kept their recipes in their heads. The dyeing occupation was inherited by sons from fathers, and they absorbed the knowledge deeply and early on; it was in their blood, so to speak. It would never have occurred to them to give away their laboriously developed and tested knowledge to a writing foreigner. But in that case, for whom was this collection of recipes written? Pfister's theory is that they were written in some Egyptian temple where the priests gladly spent their time on problems related to alchemy. These written documents also contain sections about the production of pearls, gemstones, and metals.

Even though the Papyrus documents do not give us any information about the dyeing of genuine purple, they are valuable for another reason. With their many instructions about how various purple colors were made with the help of simpler dyestuffs than mullosk secretions, they tell us that during the great age of purple dyeing, imitations and forgeries were already produced on a large scale.

Purple as a Color Definition

When we use the word purple in daily speech, we believe it stands for a quite well-defined and singular color designation. However, this is not the case. With a purple secretion as a starting material, it is possible to produce an entire range of color tones and nuances. The nature of the secretion, the mordant, and the dyeing method all play a decisive role in the appearance of the purple-dyed fiber.

It is also very clear that during antiquity there were special terms for the various colors that dyers could produce. The writer Marcus Vitruvius clearly distinguished between red Tyrian purple and blue hyacinthine purple, and in a decree the Emperor Diocletian mentions an additional number of different purple tones of varying coloristic appearance. The Old Testament speaks about blue purple *(tekhelet)* and red purple *(argaman)* in the same manner as the account about Mardukaj, which was told earlier. (See page 21.)

If we satisfy ourselves with a more general and imprecise description of the purple colors, we can say that they are all found within the blue-red part of the color scale. It may be important to keep in mind that we study the many imitations that were produced at the same time and alongside true purple. The starting material, technique, and requirements for use changed greatly, and the colors obtained are likely to have turned many different nuances. Nevertheless they all laid claims to the name purple.

The purple color could, depending of the type of mollusk and the method used, vary from a dazzling bluish red color to a reddish dark blue tone. The colored surface of the photo shows the approximate color range of the purple dye.

About Forgeries and Imitations

There were many reasons for producing forgeries and imitations of purple, mainly the high price of the products that were dyed with mollusk purple. Another reason is that the mollusks became scarce in certain areas due to intense harvesting. As mentioned earlier, this is the reason that two types of purple mollusks were wiped out by the Phoenicians. With plant dyestuffs like madder, alkanet, ochril, and kermes, possibly in combination with indigo, you could get the same color in an easier manner and at a considerably lower cost. How the colorfastness of the colors obtained was rated is unknown.

From the texts of the Old Testament and Pliny, and through archeological discoveries, we know that unspun wool was often used for dyeing. Carding together the woad-indigo blue loose wool with madder or kermes red wool resulted in a purple color with a dominant blue or red whole tone depending on the proportions of the various colors used. Carding together a madder-colored and an indigo-colored wool had a much more colorfast, violet tone, even if the dyestuff was put on the same fiber using two different baths.

Another possibility was to dye over a red-dyed yarn with woad-indigo, or the other way around. The result became a "purple color" which, just like the others, was impossible to visibly distinguish from the real thing.

The substances madder, alkanet, and kermes are mordant dyestuffs, the blue-colored woad and indigo are vat colors (see glossary), which is why a material cannot be dyed in one and the same bath. The dyeing must be done in two separate processes, one for mordant and the other for vat colors. It doesn't matter much with which one you start. Both alkanet and orchil certainly produce acceptable purple colors, but their fastness is not as good. However, the combination of madder and woad-indigo or kermes and woad-indigo gave dyeings very good properties.

"Then they brought them into the temple of the Lord, and the high-priest said: "Cast lots before me you who shall weave the gold, the white, the flax, the silk, the dark blue, the scarlet red, and the purple red.' And the purple red and the scarlet red fell to Mary's lot. And she took them and carried them home to her house.

And she took the pot and went out to draw water. Then a voice said to her: "Be saluted, you among women.' And Mary looked around to the right and left to discover where the voice came from. And she became afraid and went into the house, put down the pot, took the purple red and sat on the chair and began to spin.

And she finished the purple red and the scarlet red and carried it to the high-priest. And the high-priest took it and blessed her and said: 'Mary, Lord God has made your name great, and you shall be blessed among all the people of the world."

— Apocrypha:
James' Protevangelon

James' Protevangelon. *The majority of the gospel from which this text came is believed to have been written around the middle of the 100s.*

Hard-to-Analyze Imitations

A method that purple forgers certainly used was to add indigo to a bath of red Tyrian purple. The operation is completely possible, technically, and should not have caused the dyers any major problems. The imitations produced in this manner cannot be separated from authentic hyacinthine purple. The reasons will be covered in a later section. (See page 190.) There are two different processes where combining indigo with kermes can produce an identical color, but the imitation can be exposed through treatment with a blind vat which has the ability to dissolve the vat color.

A Ban of Dubious Value

The many forgeries and imitations that appeared in growing numbers created economic and other problems for the emperor's purple monopoly. An attempt was made to restrict the undesired competition in various manners. One of the more dubious methods was to pass laws forbidding the use of alum for treating purple within certain areas and by certain dye works. Thus, alum appears not to have been used in Palmyra in Syria during the first century B.C. The textiles from that time period found in Palmyra are believed to have been dyed with genuine mollusk purple.

Alkanet, Anchusa tinctoria.

Palmyra, "The Queen of the Desert," Syria.

Recipes from *Papyrus Holmiensis*

Several of the collection's recipes intended for use in the production of purple imitations are reproduced here.

Dyeing of Purple

"Phyrgian stone (alum) is decomposed and is allowed to simmer in a water bath. The wool is put into the bath and is allowed to stand there until it gets cold. Then take it out. In another vessel add some orchil and some amarant flowers (love-lies-bleeding). Then allow it to simmer, add the wool to it, and allow the bath to cool off. Take it out and rinse it with cold salt water."

Commentary

The orchil dyestuff that is found in several of the Papyrus' manuscript recipes comes from various types of lichen in the Mediterranean area, primarily the orchil lichen *Rosella tinctoria.* The dyestuff is not found in finished form in the plant, but must be derived by treating the dried and ground lichen with urine and, in some cases, also lime. The orchil dyestuff can give clear, deep, nearly brilliant purple or violet colors, but the fastness to light is very low. More recent experimental research by the textile artist Kerstin Gustafsson using *Rocella canariensis* from the island of El Hierro (the Canary Islands) and a new technique with a higher temperature and a longer dyeing time has given remarkably high test value.

Salt water is believed to have the ability to attach itself to the wool fiber while the pores are open during dyeing, in order to create a color with better resistance to tearing.

Dyeing of Tyrian or Guaranteed Excellent Purple

"Take this formula: 1 drachma "Alkan" (1 Roman drachma was about 7.5 pounds/3.4 kilograms), 5 drachmas "operment,"5 drachmas of unslaked lime, a smaller amount of urine and (the necessary amount) of water."

Commentary

The alkanet dyestuff is obtained from the ground root bark of *Anchusa tinctoria*, which grows wild in southern Europe and Asia. It produces blue-violet to almost black colors. The light resistance is not as good, however.

The value of the addition of "operment" in the recipe is not made clear. "Operment," which is called arsenious sulphide today, was previously called "orpiment," "auripigment," and other names. Despite its toxicity, it was used in older times in tanneries and dye works, and, among other things, as a reducing agent in dyeing indigo, and possibly also as a mordant.

Yarn dyed with orchil lichen, Rocella canariensis, *from the island of El Hierro (the Canary Islands).*

COCHINEAL – KERMES – LACCA

BOTANIQUE.

DICOTYLÉDONES.   Cactoïdes. *(Vent.)*

Turpin pinx.t et direx.t   *Massard sculp.t*

CACTIER à cochenilles.
CACTUS cochenillifer. *(Lin.)*
(⁴⁄₅ Grand.nat.)

Cochineal scale insect,
Dactylopius coccus, *on a*
flowering Opuntia cactus.
From French flora, circa 1800.

Cochineal

The Color Scale Insect
from the Old and New Worlds

When we color today's textiles we do it with the help of a number of artificially produced dyestuffs, or what we call "synthetic colors" in everyday language. For over a century we have made use of that possibility. If we are asked for some reason what was used in earlier cultures, the spontaneous answer is, almost without exception, that dyestuffs from various plants were used.

What many people no longer remember is that several of the most important dyestuffs from the earliest times did not come from the plant world but are, instead, of animal origin. This is above all true of dyes intended for the red and blue color areas. The best known is without a doubt the purple color described earlier, but there are also a number of colors that could be derived from various types of so-called color scale insects from both the Old and the New worlds. Together with indigo, purple, and madder, they comprise the most worthy and most used dyestuffs throughout time.

The Gold That Did Not Glitter

A color plant, a mollusk, or a scale insect does not announce, through its leaves, fruits, or glands, the presence of any dyestuff. Only the dyer knows that, through his chemical manipulations, brilliant and hardy colors can be derived from the often unattractive natural materials. One day in the middle of the 1700s, the crew of one of the Caribbean's most feared pirate ships learned that both colorful and pecuniary riches could be hidden in very humble dress. They sighted a large Spanish ship outside the coast of Honduras with a presumed load of gold and silver intended to enrich the Spanish crown, a circumstance of ownership that they decided to change rapidly by catching up with and boarding the ship. The Spaniards were quick and managed to avoid their pursuers.

In their haste to escape, the longboat was left behind and was captured by the pursuers. The pirates' disappointment over having captured only a longboat filled with worthless bags of dried brown grain quickly changed to happiness when they realized that the contents consisted of the "scarlet grain" — the fabulous, expensive raw material for the red dyestuff carmine!

At the time of this event the origin of the "scarlet grain" was still unknown in Europe. However, rumor had it that the Spaniards got it, along with other precious goods, far away in the mysterious countries on the other side of the Atlantic.

Pre-Columbian band from Pachacamac, Peru. The band is woven in tapestry technique on hard-twined, naturally dyed, beige-white cotton warp. The weft mainly consists of two-ply wool yarn, with some smaller sections woven from yarn that is twined from one wool thread and one cotton thread. The pink, brownish pink, and blue violet threads are all dyed with cochineal. Dyestuff analysis also revealed iron in the dark violet threads, which indicates it was used as a mordant.

The Areas of Origin
and the Early Use of Cochineal

The valuable but outwardly insignificant small grain was nothing other than dried females of the insect family *Dactylopius,* long called cochineal. Despite the fact that cochineal had been introduced to Europe before the end of the 1500s, uncertainty about the true nature of the dyestuff reigned long into the 1700s. The cause was simple enough. For the Spaniards, the sought-after good was of the greatest economic importance and they did everything they could to keep its existence and production a secret. Various written Spanish sources from the 1500s give evidence of the sensitive nature of the substance. Early works kept silent or were directly misleading about actual conditions. Later, what were for the most part correct descriptions, remained unnoticed or not believed. In fact, the Spanish authorities encouraged this lack of knowledge, making it more difficult for foreigners to gain a collective picture of the manner of production and work methods used in cochineal factories.

Dried cochineal in a Peruvian clay pan. In the background a map of the parts of Central America where cochineal dye is produced.

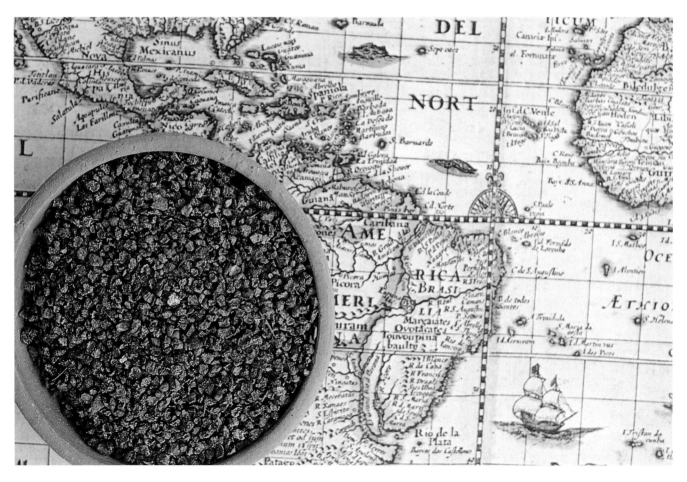

The cochineal scale insect originates in South and Central America, where the Indians already used the carmine color for dyeing textiles in 1000 B.C. When the Spaniards went to Mexico in the early 1500s, the dyestuff became frequently used. From Mexico its use spread to other countries, including Peru. The old Aztec term for color was *Nochezli,* which the Spaniards changed to *cochinilla.* Eventually the French form of the word, *cochenille,* became the most used.

The cochineal scale insect belongs to the *coccidae* family and is related to *Dactylopius* (Costa); this name now replaces earlier names, including Linné's *Coccus cacti*. The males are grayish red in color, about .1 of an inch (2 to 3 mm) long and their wings are membranes coated with a fine substance. The females are dark bluish red, wingless, .1 to .16 inches (3 to 4 mm) long and have a short suction proboscis with which they suck in their nourishment from the host plant. One male comes to 300 females. After becoming pregnant, the backs of the females' bodies swell up significantly as they fill with eggs. This is the stage during which they are collected.

Silk and silver brocade, fragment from Venice, 1500-1600s. Dyestuff analysis revealed that the red color was dyed with cochineal.

Breeding, Harvesting, and Drying

Fragment of the border of a cloak from Peru with the pre-Peruvian deity Kon-Tiki as motif. Dated to the 700s. Analysis showed that the red color was produced with cochineal.

The cochineal lives on two closely related types of cactuses, *Opuntia* and *Nopalea*. The latter is the host plant for eight to nine types of cochineal, the former for over 200. Both types of cactuses have been bred and used since pre-Columbian times. The wild cochineal can be collected all year long from the host plant, the wild growing *Nopalea*-cactus. The bred types are collected during special harvest seasons, usually two to four per year. During each harvest a certain number of females are left behind to ensure that the strain survives.

Based on Spanish descriptions from the 1500s, it can be concluded that, early on, the "scarlet grain" was the object of regular and well organized breeding on a large scale. In an account from about 1630, Thomas Gager wrote the following about the province of Zoques. "The most important products are silk and cochineal, of which the latter was regarded as the best in America, and the production is so large that no other province exceeds it. There are few Indians who haven't planted their fields with the trees (cactuses) on which these grubs (insects) feed . . . not that the Indians themselves value it in any other way than that the Spaniards desire it and offer money for it, and prevail upon them to breed it in those parts of the country that have demonstrated themselves to be the most successful for such business. . ."

Of course, a product that was as profitable as cochineal had to be handled with great care. In a work from 1781, R. Landivar thus gives the advice: ". . .when a rainstorm sweeps in over the wide field, or hail threatens the plantation, they should be protected with bast mats, the way the Indians do it. These clever people have placed tall wooden sticks on the sides of the cactus plants and placed bast mats on these for permanent protection; the mats can be pulled over the plants with the help of a rope. . ."

The collection of the egg-filled females took place through careful removal from the segments of the cactus with a feather pen from a bird, a pointed pin, or a paintbrush, and were collected in small wooden, braided straw, or pottery containers.

The collected insects could be killed in various manners. The simplest and possibly the oldest method was to spread them out on sack cloths or bast mats that were then placed under the heat of the sun in the warm sand. By this method the so-called silver gray cochineal *(Plateada blanca)* was obtained. This process (and variations of it) could take up to two weeks and were considered to give the best products. In 1573, the Spanish authorities attempted to prohibit other methods, but without success. One such method, for example, was to kill the insects using hot steam, after which they were dried in the sun or in hot ovens.

In certain locations they were killed on sheet metal that was held over a fire. The cochineal grain became dark brown to black from this process.

Forms of Sales, Names, and Appearance

As a trade good, the cochineal consisted of small, shriveled, round grains, the appearance of which varied according to the various methods of treatment that were applied when killing and drying them. The size of the grain varied a great deal: the largest of the bred forms *(Grana fina, G. mestica)* contains more dyestuff and is more valuable than the wild kind *(Grana silvestra)*.

In addition, after dyeing the cochineal was classified according to the type of production and according to the harvest. Insects from the first harvest were greater and more valuable than those collected from later harvests, which were called *Saccatilla*. Honduran or Guatemalan *Saccatilla* were considered the best. These types were made of nearly black, dyestuff rich, large grains.

Fragment of a damask weave from Spain dated to the 1500s. Analysis showed that American cochineal was used for the red color.

Cochineal Forgeries

As a result of the high prices that the cochineal grain commanded, forgeries soon became common and the authorities continually feared them. From the end of the 1500s, we can read about various forms for these deceptions. In one place it is mentioned that chalk and pulverized clay were being used, but pitch, sand and other things were also selected in accordance with the looks and color of the cochineal. Worse types could also contain plant fragments and insect parts that were put there for the sole purpose of making the product heavier.

One of the more refined methods was used in England on a large scale during part of the 1800s. Dyestuff from the cochineal scale insect was partially extracted with alcohol. The insect, which was apparently still intact, could then be disposed of.

R.A. Donkin, from whose study of cochineal several of the older quotes in this work came, writes the following plausible commentary about the forgeries. "In reality, cases of forgeries were numerous, but what was done about them in New Spain (Mexico) was apparently insignificant compared to what often happened after this product arrived in Europe."

Red from the Other Side of the Ocean

The Latin American countries' original production of cochineal should have been limited in scope and only intended to meet the needs of domestic textile production. After the Spaniards arrived, large-scale production of this valuable dyestuff was introduced and it eventually became one of the most important sources of income for the colonial power, aside from the export of silver. It has been calculated that between the years of 1758 and 1858, no less than 27,000 tons of cochineal were shipped out of Mexico. The picture of the extent of cochineal production becomes even clearer if data about the size of the plantations is considered. Each plantation consisted of no less than 50,000 cactus plants. The increasing demand was partly because the European and the Asian dye works discovered that Mexican cochineal had a higher content of active dyestuff than the Polish and Armenian color scale kermes insects which had been used up to that time.

Thus, export was to Europe alone. In the 1580s, cochineal was transferred with loads of silver from

Acapulco on the Tehuantepec isthmus to Manila on the Philippines. The dyestuff was also found in China from the time of the emperor Kang-Hsis (1662-1722). This far-sighted ruler was not only the promoter of the first great Chinese map and a great literary encyclopedia of over 5,000 volumes, but he was also the one who gave the French and British the right to conduct trade between China and the Occident. He was aware that *Ko-tcha-ni-la* was a product of a Latin American insect and that it was introduced by the Europeans. The carmine color went (and still goes) under the name of "foreign root," *Yang Hung. Yang* actually means ocean, so the expression could also be translated as "red from the other side of the ocean." Compare this to our word ultramarine (the blue gemstone lapis lazuli, from the other side of the ocean).

The Spread of the Cochineal Scale Insect to New Areas

The Spaniards brought the dried cochineal insect to Europe where the carmine dyestuff was then extracted, packed, and sold to waiting consumers. To ensure sole right to the product, the Spanish government prohibited all forms of import of living scale insects to the European continent.

Despite constant prohibitions that included a ban on exporting the mother strain of cochineal from Mexico to bordering Latin American areas, by the end of the 1700s, breeding had spread across the borders of the country to Guatemala, Brazil, and to the Indonesian island of Java. Later, plantations were also started on several of the West Indian islands, in Algeria, and on the Canary Islands. The monopoly that the Spaniards had ever since Cortéz conquered Mexico in 1519 was thereby broken, and the consumers could be supplied with the cochineal dyestuff from a number of different markets: the French from Veracruz, the Dutch from Java, and the English from India.

The Breeding of Cochineal in Europe

The introduction of cochineal breeding in Europe was not a completely painless process. The Spaniards carefully guarded all spread of knowledge concerning the "scarlet grain" and were opposed to the export of the living insect. On top of this, there were difficulties with acclimatizing the insects and the host plants to the intended breeding grounds. Of course it was impossible to maintain opposition to export for long, and in the year 1777, a French royal botanist was successful in smuggling out a small number of living cochineal after a research trip to Mexico. He attempted to begin breeding it on the then French colony of Haiti, but the experiment failed. Later, French attempts to breed the cochineal scale insect on imported *Opuntia* cactuses in Algeria and on

Madagascar also failed. The cactuses did well, but the worthy insect could not acclimatize to the new environments.

The Breeding of Cochineal on the Canary Islands

On the other hand, the Spaniards were significantly more successful than the French at establishing breeding in new areas. Certainly an early experiment (1820), with importation to the sunny coast of Malaga did not work very well. The Spanish cochineal could not compete with other cochineal on the world market due to high production costs and low insect yield. But a few years before Mexico gained its independence from Spain in 1836, a new attempt was made to transplant the Mexican cochineal, this time on the Canary Islands. The Opuntia cactus had already been introduced there because of its edible fruit (the so-called cactus fig). And this time the transplantation succeeded beyond all expectations. The insect did well, increased rapidly, and spread to new areas. However, no regular breeding like there was in Mexico took place until the 1830s, and great skepticism ruled about the cochineal scale insect in the beginning, and many considered it harmful to grapes and other necessary crops.

After some farsighted field owners demonstrated that cochineal of high quality could be produced and sold at a good profit, circumstances rapidly changed. The now entirely Spanish production of the carmine dyestuff was encouraged in this area because, at that time, many South American countries changed over to growing coffee on a large scale. The Canary Islands eventually became the world's leading supplier of cochineal.

Cochineal production on Java

The breeding of cochineal on Java was carried out in the province of Bantam and in the area around the old sultan city Cheribon (Cirebon) on the southwestern coast of the Java Sea. It took one-and-one-half years for the host cactuses to reach full maturity, and they needed half a year to recover after each insect harvest. After eight years they were replaced by new plants. The cochineal completed their life cycles in the relatively short period of about two months, during which time they were protected by braided straw baldachin over the host plants. They were killed and dried in the sun for 14 days or in warm ovens for several weeks, then sorted according to quality. The majority were exported to China and Holland.

Opuntia cactus. *From Herbarium Mathiolo camerariani , 1596.*

Carl von Linné's
Unsuccessful Introduction of Cochineal

Carl von Linné was greatly inspired by the mercantile spirit of the 1700s that left its mark on everything classified and all recommendations for the improvement of our sustenance. Dyeing was of great interest to him, and he became a pioneer and one of the field's most prolific writers. In numerous written documents, particularly his famous "travels," he describes our "dye-grass" and the manner in which it was used. Along with his pupils, he eagerly searched for the kind of plants, lichen, etc. that could be used in dyeing. He also recorded the dyeing methods that had previously only been partially described.

One of the most expensive imported dyestuffs was cochineal. It came to Sweden in double-sealed sacks, so-called "serons" which weighed 100 "skålpund" (42.5 kg) when full. Linné's intention was to study them more carefully, and he even decided to breed the insect in question (in a greenhouse of course).

One spring day in 1755, one of Linné's pupils, Daniel Rolander, who was also his son's tutor, left for Surinam in South America, to find living cochineal (among other things) for his master to study. The following year Rolander sent home a large pot with an *Opuntia* cactus planted in it, which was filled with living cochineal scale insects. The expensive and fragile package landed in Uppsala after many difficulties, where it was delivered to a botanical garden. The *Opuntia* was received by the gardener who discovered that the plant was full of "vermin" and decided to rinse it clean. He did this so thoroughly that not one single insect was left when Linné came to see the longed-for insects. After a careful search, a single specimen was found. It was a female, but unfortunately she was not pregnant. Linné lamented that he was the first person to see "cochineal in Europe living; but no longer." It is easy to understand why the mishap grieved him, when you consider the communication difficulties in those days. "All hope disappeared," he said, and the misfortune touched him so deeply that he "got a migraine and one of the most difficult paroxysms he knew."

The Use of Cochineal Today

The strong red carmine dyestuff of cochineal has almost completely been replaced by cheaper and easier-to-handle synthetically produced colors. But the demand has never completely disappeared; in fact, the need for natural dyestuffs has even increased because more countries have introduced prohibitions against the use of synthetic colors in foods, cosmetics, and medicines. There is also a group of loyal users all over the world who prefer to dye their yarns and woven materials with natural dyestuffs. In addition, 70 percent of the material in modern Persian rugs is still dyed with plant dyestuffs. Therefore cochineal breeding still takes place in Central America and on the Canary Islands, and it looks as if the Mexican gift of "the scarlet grain's" red color is here to stay.

The Revolutionary Mistake
of Drebbel the Chemist

In a work about kermes and cochineal, published in London in 1846, John Beckmann wrote the following.

"The tincture of cochineal alone yields a purple colour, not very pleasant, which may be heightened to the most beautiful scarlet by a solution of tin in aqua-regia (hydrochloric acid and nitric acid). This invention may be considered among the most important improvements

Cochineal and alkanet-dyed yarn.

in the art of dyeing, and deserves a particular relation." The story of this important discovery follows.

A well-known Dutch chemist, Cornelius Drebbel, had one day placed a vessel of carmine-colored alcohol, intended for use in a thermometer, in his laboratory window. From a damaged glass container a small amount of the aqua regia dropped down into a solution, causing the liquid to change from a purple color to a strong red color. On closer investigation and after some experiments, Drebbel was able to determine that tin from joints of the lead bars on the window dissolved in the aqua regia, causing dramatic and unexpected color change. He reported his suspicions about the sequence of events to the expert dyer Kuffelar in Leyden, who later became his son-in-law. Kuffelar perfected the discovery and managed to keep it a secret for some years in his own dye works. The color first became known as Dutch scarlet, but later on it was marketed under the name of Kuffelar's Color.

After just ten years the secret became known among dyers in London and Paris. Louis XIV's financial advisor, Jean Baptiste Colbert, helped to introduce the dye to the state-owned Manufacture Nationale des Gobelins, where the color became known as Gobelin-scarlet. In 1643 in the town of Bow near London, a Flemish dyer established the first dye works with scarlet dyeing as a speciality. At first the English called it the "Bow-Color."

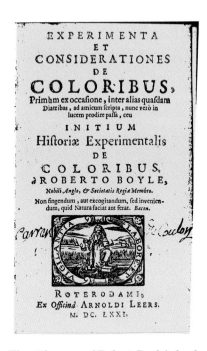

The title page of Robert Boyle's book, Historiae de Experimentalis de Coloribus*, Rotterdam, 1671.*

The Thoughts of Other Chemists Regarding Tin in Dyeing

The natural scientist Robert Boyle (1627-1691), often called the father of chemistry, and one of the founders of the London's Royal Society, points out in one of his works, *Experimenta de Coloribus*, that a bright scarlet color can only be obtained if tin-plated receptacles are used in dyeing. He may have observed the color-enhancing effect that the presence of tin had in dyeing treatment.

Another dyeing technology author, Claude Louis Berthollet, considered the greatest of the French dye chemists, also belongs to those who have observed the significance of tin. He pointed out that kermes, if it was dyed with a tin pre-mordant material, gave a nuance that was just as clear as cochineal.

Finally a few lines from the 1840 handbook for dyers by the British chemist and dyer Thomas Packer will be quoted. "It is necessary to remember, that the best container for dyeing scarlet is one of pure tin. The dyers of the East India Company used such containers."

Old Cochineal Recipes

Genuine Crimson on Wool

—According to Cajsa Warg, 1762

For a "skålpund" of yarn you take two "Lod" of white wine stone, 2 "Lod" of red wine stone, 4 "Lod" of Roman alum, and 4 handfuls of wheat bran, which is boiled in 4 "kanna" of water and stirred well. Then the yarn is added: boil for 1½ hours, working it well. Then take it out, and hang it on a pole overnight, and rinse it out the next day. The same day that the yarn boils, soften 2 "Lod" of finely pounded cochineal in ½ "Stop" of water. On the second day, put it into a kettle along with 3 "kannor" of water, one "Qwintin" of white wine stone, one "Quintin" of red wine stone, 2 "Lod" of white strengthener, 1 "Qwintin" of red Arianicum. This is boiled together, the yarn is added and allowed to boil for one hour while it is worked well, after which it is taken out to cool and be rinsed.

Commentary

Wine stone was previously made from wine and took its color from that. The red wine stone is made from red wines and usually came from Bordeaux, whereas the white wine stone originated from Rhine or other white wines.

In handbooks about dyeing with natural dyestuffs, from older or newer times, wine stone with alum is usually recommended for the mordanting process. Many have also, although nobody has demonstrated its actual purpose in dyeing, conveyed the impression that wine stone was also a mordant, which was not the case. Instead the wine stone is what we call a dyeing and mordanting aid.

Chemically, the wine stone works by keeping the metal salts — alum for example — in solution. Otherwise they could easily precipitate out of solution, forming an insoluble combination which can no longer influence the fiber. When we use wine stone it is also a means of ensuring that the amount of mordants added to the bath really attach themselves to the fibers, so that mordanting is not weaker than anticipated, giving a weaker dyeing.

Alum appears in older literature about dyeing under a variety of different names. Some allude to a certain level of quality, others to the area of production, and still others on the form of the alum crystals. The expression "Roman alum," which appears in the recipe above, can be interpreted here to mean alum of very good quality, that is as clean and free of iron as possible, although it is not necessarily produced in Rome. Before 1400, what was meant by Roman alum was a product that came from Constantinople and later on from the Tolfa alum works north of Rome.

At the Garphyttans' alum works in Närke, alum was produced during the 1700s and 1880s according to instructions from the mining advisor Sven Rinman. It was considered as good as, or even better than, the Roman alum. In a testimonial Malmsten, the manager of the "Färgeristat" in Stockholm wrote the following about the alum: "I have tried it in cloth, silk, and wool dyeing, and I have found that all parts where alum is used correspond exactly to the fineness and strength of the alum imported from Civita Vecchia, under the name of Roman, used in our dye works up to now."

Genuine Scarlet Color on Wool

—According to Cajsa Warg, 1762

Add 2 "Lod" of finely pestled white wine stone and 1 handful of wheat bran to one "skålpund" of prepared wool yarn that has been manufactured into vests, socks, or knitted socks. Stir this together in a kettle that is well coated with tin; add 3 "kannor" of water and let it boil, and stir it well with a stick. Then you put the wool yarn in it and let it boil for 1 hour, while frequently stirring (up and down). Then you remove it and let it hang overnight. The second day you rinse it well and let it drain. The following day when you let the yarn boil, you take the second "Lod" of nitric acid and 4 "Lods" of other pure water, and put it together in a flask. Then take ½ "Lod" of English tin, drop it into the water slowly like hail, add the nitric acid, and let it stand for twenty-four hours. When it has been standing that long, you pour off the clear and throw away the thick sludge; and the same day that the nitric acid transforms, add the second "Lod" of cochineal, which is pounded very fine. Strain through a gauze sieve, and put it in ½ "Stop" of water, which should stand over night. The second day you add 3 "kannor" of water into a pre-heated kettle and cochineal into it, boil it together, separate off the scum by stirring often, and add the nitric acid to this, and stir well. Then you put in the yarn, which is boiled ½ hour. Stir often during the boiling, but afterwards cool and rinse it off.

Commentary

The reason for the wheat bran that is supposed to be added at the beginning of this recipe is to make the water suitable for dyeing. In his handbook for dyers, the British dyer and chemist Thomas Packer wrote about this. "A dyer can never be too careful in selecting the water he needs. . ." He recommends that the water be heated up together with a bag of bran. ". . . During this operation the elements that are harmful for dyeing will form a scum which should be removed just before the water begins to boil."

Later in the recipe the ingredient nitric acid is mentioned, by which is meant the tin solution that "brings forth" the scarlet red color. The tin solution, which is also called composition or tin solution, was previously made by dissolving pulverized tin in nitric acid, which was diluted with a double quantity of clean, soft (preferably distilled) water. The acid should not be too strong or too warm, because this might cause the tin to precipitate, that is, be converted to an insoluble form.

Weight and volume measurements: 1 "skålpund" = 425 g; 1 "lod" = 13.3 g; 1 "kanna" = 2.6 l; 1 "stop" = 1.3 l

"Kermes:
A Color More Beautiful Than Purple"

—John Beckmann, 1846

Velvet brocade fragment from Italy, 1400s. Dyestuff analysis showed that the red color was dyed with Kermes vermilis.

The Attention-Getting Gift of the Persian Ruler

In one of his documents, the Sicilian author from the 300s, Flavius Vopiscus, tells how on one occasion the Persian ruler sent the Emperor Marcus Aurelius some woolen cloth which had a more beautiful and brighter purple red color than any previously seen in the Roman Empire! Compared to these textiles, the purple clothing worn by the emperor and the ladies of the court appeared dull and faded. Experienced dyers were sent from Rome to India to seek what they believed to be the color purple, as well knowledge of the dyeing method. However, they returned without having found the article, and could only leave a vague report that basically stated that the Persian "purple" was produced from some sort of a plant.

According to professor John Beckmann of the University in Göttingen in the early 1800s, the sensational textiles were not dyed with mollusk purple, but with a color from the colored scale insect kermes! This story comes from his book, *The History of Inventions and Discoveries, 1783-1805* (published in London, 1846). The same is true for many other interesting statements about the kermes scale insect, which will be commented on in the following.

Beckmann points out the Romans themselves used kermes for dyeing during that period, and that is must have been relatively easy for them to obtain kermes. But they were so bad at the art of dyeing that they could only use it as a base color for subsequent dyeing with purple. It must have seemed unbelievable to them that people in far off India could use it to produce a color that was more beautiful than purple itself. He also believed that this is because the Greeks and Romans were unfamiliar with the effects of acid on kermes, something that the Indians and Persians knew.

Some observations can be added to Beckmann's thoughts. It is not acid alone that makes the red color more brilliant and highly colorfast. The acids favorably promote the effect of the dye on the fiber, in the same way that coloring with the chemically similar carmine does. The result is a deeper and more saturated color. But a prerequisite is that you treat the yarn in an effective manner (with alum or preferably tin). Alum salt is the oldest and most used tanners mordant throughout history for various wool fibers. Without it you get a color that lacks depth and fastness.

Opposite page: Twist seam embroidery fragment from Perugia, Italy dated to the 1400s. According to analysis, dyed with a lac scale insect dyestuff, possibly Armenian Kermes.

My hypothesis is that the dyers in the Orient knew about some form of mordant tin preparation early on. Through its use, it should be possible to produce the dramatically increased brilliance and clarity of the kermes red color, which so obviously separated the gift of the Persian ruler from Marcus Aurelius' purple toga. But knowing of the Indian and Persian dyers as yet unsurpassed technical knowledge about dyeing, it seems easonable to think that they were successful in solving that problem. Centuries ago people were successful in putting the strong red madder dyestuff on a cellulose fiber (primarily cotton) using a trick in a complicated process. A method that was brought to the Occident much later and the result of which we know under the name of India red or Turkey red.

Kermes: A Seed or Just a Grub?

There was a great deal of doubt among the authors of antiquity at the beginning of our chronology as to whether kermes was an insect or part of a plant. In connection with the production of "double purple," Pliny mentions that a type of "red pit or seed, called *coccum,* from Galatia or Merida in Lusitania" was used. He continues the description ". . . to conclude speaking about this famous dyestuff, it is the seed that, when it is a year old, contains a viscous juice, but it begins to disappear after it has turned four years old." What Pliny is referring to here is apparently nothing other than the color scale insect kermes.

The Greek natural scientist Theophrastus, a friend and pupil of Aristotle and sometimes called the father of Botany, wrote that the kermes oak has "a type of red berry." The botanist and pharmacologist Dioscordes, a contemporary of Pliny, was equally uncertain. In one of his works he calls kermes *coccus baphike,* that is color berry. Other authors describe kermes as a type of grub. The account of these changing points of view can continue with additional examples. Even if they quarreled over whether it was a berry or a grub, they agreed that the kermes was found on a low sort of brushlike tree with thorny leaves that belonged to the oak family. There is no reason to doubt that they meant the low evergreen *Quercus ilex.*

The kermes scale insect's host plant, from Herbarium Mathiolo camerariani, *1596.*

58

The Color Scale Insect from the Foot of Mt. Ararat

The educated people of antiquity knew kermes well, calling it *coccum* or *coccus* and sometimes *granum*. But knowledge of its true nature was long characterized by great uncertainty. Writings on the topic are full of mistakes and contradictions. For this and other reasons, we will only discuss some of the most important and best known of the kermes scale insects. *Kermes vermilis (Kermococcus vermilis)*, which lives on the kermes oak *(Quercus coccifera)*, and *Kermes ilicis*, which has another type of oak as a host tree *(Q. ilex)* are generally considered among the most common types. However, there are divided opinions about whether the latter type of kermes gives a perfect carmine dyestuff. Both insects and host plants are found around the coast of the Mediterranean in certain places in the Middle East.

In northern parts of Israel there are also several types of insects that contain a red dyestuff: *Kermes biblicus*, which lives on *Q. calliprinos* and *Kermes spatulatus* which is found on *Q. ithaburensis*.

Several varieties of kermes live on host plants that are completely different from oaks. One of the most well-known is Turkish or Armenian kermes *(kirmiz)* which lives on various types of grasses *(Aeluropis laevis* and *Dactylis litoralis* , etc.) that grow in Armenia and in the area around Ararat. For more than two thousand years the red carmine color has been produced at the foot of Mt. Ararat.

Mt. Ararat

The Development, Harvest, and Trade of Kermes

The mating of the kermes scale insect takes place in the month of April and the males die shortly after. The fertilized females grow quickly to small, round balls the size of a pea. Egg laying takes place in the beginning of June with up to three thousand eggs per insect, after which the females also die and dry up to empty, grey-white shells. As soon as the female larvae develop, they find a suitable place on the host plant to attach themselves and remain there for the rest of their lives. The female kermes does not have wings, while the males, who are significantly fewer, develop the wings that make it possible to find the waiting females in April.

The collection of female kermes took place right before egg laying in May. In France and other southern European countries, the women employed in collecting the insects let their nails grow long to facilitate the job. The harvested insects were killed with steam from boiling wine vinegar or by drowning them in a mixture of wine vinegar and water. In this process their original black violet color changed to a reddish brown color. They were then dried in the sun, pulverized, and packed. No less than 50,000 to 60,000 insects were used to make one kilogram of carmine dyestuff.

The name carmine has long been used for two dyestuffs that are closely related to that of the color scale insect: carmine acid and kermes acid. The previously described cochineal scale insect contains carmine acid, while the kermes scale insect (the one that uses various types of oaks as host plants) give kermes acid. The root kermes scale insects, like Polish kermes, contain both types of dyestuff.

Kermes is primarily used for dyeing wool and silk, and the dyestuff has an aromatic odor that is transferred to the textile during the dyeing process. Kermes was also frequently used in folk medicines, primarily in connection with treating wounds by causing contractions.

Johannesblod: Polish Kermes

The types of kermes that have been mentioned up to now all live on the parts of host plants that are above ground But there are also types that live on the roots of certain plants. This is the case with the insect that goes under the name of Polish kermes (*Margarodes polonicus* and *Porphyrophorus polonicus*), which live on the root system of the perennial host plant, knavel *(Sclerantus perennis)*. Both belong to eastern parts of Europe, mainly eastern Germany (Saxony), Poland, Lithuania, and the Ukraine.

The collection of this root kermes was extraordinarily labor intensive, because the plants had to be dug up by their roots first, the insects picked off, and then replanted. A good collector could harvest more than 50-100 grams of insects in a day. These were then killed in the same manner as other types of kermes, with the help of vinegar solution or by subjecting them to vinegar steam vapor.

Johannesblod

Because the harvest took place around Midsummer, around St. Johns day, the Polish kermes was named Johannesblod. Beckmann (1792) was of the opinion that "the clergy wished by that appellation to make this revenue appear as a matter of religion." At that time, many monasteries in Eastern Europe had their subordinates collect these insects, and paid for the harvest in tithes. Those who didn't bring a sufficient number had to pay a certain amount of money instead.

It is hard to determine when Polish kermes began to be used, and the sources are unfortunately not in complete agreement about this. Some think that the industry must date to at least the beginning of our chronology, and that the Chinese had it already during the first centuries AD. None of the Greek, Roman, or Arabian authors mention any form of root kermes. In the *Beschreibung von Allerley Insekten*, Berlin 1736, we get our first description of how harvesting took place in the Germany of the 1100s.

The production of root kermes was encouraged by the high price that the product commanded and its high quality made it one of the coveted colors. During the 1700s considerable quantities went to silk and velvet textile factories in Venice. According to some sources, sales continued as late as the early 1800s.

Finally several additional types of root kermes will be mentioned: *Coccus fragariae*, which lives on Siberian strawberry plants, and *C. uva ursi*, which lives in Russia on the roots of the bearberry.

Kermes Overtakes the Role of Purple

With the fall of the Byzantine empire and the collapse of the production of purple, the carmine from various types of kermes took over as the most important red dyestuff in the Western world. In 1467 a decree by Pope Paul II replaced the purple dye that had been used on the cardinal's gown *(mozzetta)* with scarlet, a color change that was supposed to bring the cardinals on an equal level with kings. From then on the kermes carmine was often called cardinal purple.

During the Middle Ages kermes was an unbelievably expensive dyestuff, and only the powerful in society could purchase textiles that were dyed with it. Those who wore clothing dyed with kermes were given the epithet *coccinati* — a parallel to the *purpurati* used with Roman dignitaries.

During the 1400s and 1500s, Venice assumed a leading role in the production of silk, achieving a level of silk harvesting that made importing the expensive product unnecessary. The particular suitability of carmine for dyeing silk contributed to Venice becoming a center for trade of this highly valued dyestuff in the Middle Ages, and for a long time it was called "Venetian scarlet."

There is a story that when explorer Vasco da Gama arrived in Calcutta he gave a red cloth from Venice to the first Hindu ruler he met as a gift from his regent. He was also dressed in scarlet during that audience as a sign that he represented his king. In addition to the red cloth, he gave a number of other samples of western handwork. According to contemporary sources, though, enthusiasm for the gifts was moderate.

The dyestuff was primarily brought into Venice from the Orient, while Marseille became the import area for carmine from Southwestern Europe. France, Spain, Morocco, and Algeria were the counties that produced kermes carmine, but very little is known about that.

Ships from the 13th and 14th centuries.

Edward Bancroft and William Morris on the Kermes Color

British literature about dyeing, including the works of Bancroft, often points out that a majority of dyers considered kermes the best red dyestuff, hardier than cochineal and more brilliant than madder. In the 900s kermes was commonly used in Europe. The Gothic tapestries were all dyed with it, and they have kept their red color much better than those of later works dyed with cochineal.

William Morris belonged to those who preferred the more subdued Middle Ages red dye, which was produced by, as he phrased it, "Al-kermes or coccus treated with alum in a strongly acidated bath." He had little understanding of the use of tin salt in cochineal dyeing and describes the color obtained as certainly bright, but vulgar and ugly.

Scarlet Red Patches of Cloth

In one of his short stories, the Florentine 1300's author Franco Sacchetti tells about the disrespectful use of the scarlet red color by his favorite character, the fool Ribi.

Ribi's coat was worn out and full of holes, which depressed him a great deal. The coat had actually never been particularly valuable, because it was made out of *romagnuolo,* a coarse cloth that only country people used. One day Ribi made his way to the wife of the patrician Donatis and asked for a small piece of scarlet cloth. When she asked him, in amazement, for what he intended to use such a thing — the scarlet red color was only for the richest and finest people in town — he answered, "to patch my jacket." Donna Donati certainly thought that the idea was ridiculous, but when Ribi persisted in his request, she gave him two patches, one for the hole in the chest and the other for the hole in the back.

The next morning, after Ribi carefully patched his jacket, he went to town and caused a lot of amusement. He was continually stopped by young noblemen — known in town as he was — who asked him: "What does this mean, you have patched *romagnuolo* with scarlet?" Each time they did this Ribi asked for a piece of scarlet cloth. If he got it he sewed it beside the patches he already had. Finally he had covered his entire garment with scarlet red patches and in that manner got a scarlet jacket. It probably looked multicolored, but nevertheless it was scarlet, which made him look comically pseudo-aristocratic, an effect he apparently aimed for.

"To Dye Cloth Scarlet Red in the Venetian Manner"

In 1548 a work by Gioanventura Rosetti was published in Venice entitled *Plictho de Larte de Tentori*. The work came to play a significant role in our knowledge of the art of dyeing during the latter period of the Middle Ages. It contained information about the dyestuffs and mordants of those times, as well as a large number of dye recipes. In an introductory section Rosetti also assesses the various types of kermes, designating the Armenian as one of the best, the Asiatic from an area not described in more detail as second best, and the European (Spanish) only in third place. In another place (recipe no. 88) he distinguishes between the kermes from Provence and Valencia. One formula in which kermes is used will be reproduced here in significantly abbreviated form and supplemented with some commentary.

"Scarlet Red in the Venetian Manner."
—Rosetti, 1548

"First note the weight of the cloth and then calculate 175 g of kermes for each piece of cloth. As mordant for a piece of ½ kg use 15 g Roche alum and 30 g of white wine stone, well pulverized and sifted. Fill a kettle with pure water and add the alum and wine stone. Keep a moderate fire underneath it until it begins to boil. Then put the cloth in and allow it to "boil" uninterrupted for an hour over a moderate fire. Then you have to take out the cloth and rinse it in running water and wash it well. Then put the water kettle on the fire again and add four buckets of "power water" (bran preparation). When you see that it is beginning to boil, add the kermes color, but make sure that it is sufficiently ground. Put the cloth in and hold it well below the surface and pull it four to five times on the hasp. (See sketch.) Take the cloth out and rinse it. Then give it two to three baths with wheat bran with ½ kg Roche alum and ½ kg wine stone. Then a bath with a bran without wine stone with ½ kg arsenic, well pulverized. Note that the cloth needs to cook one-fourth hour for each new bath with bran."

Commentary

This recipe shows how the famous color Venetian scarlet was produced with kermes and the necessary mordant. No other dyes, such as bresilja and orchil, have been included. It is not clear to which type of fabric the recipe refers, but we can assume that it is silk.

The mordant alum came to Venice via its colony Milos and through its trade connections from Alexandria and places on the south coast of Asia Minor as well. Roche alum, called for in the recipe, was a product of the highest quality. It was the result of a refined and detailed process that was developed at an alum boilery near Smyrna, which was started in the late 1200s.

Qui ui scriuero per ordine tutte le maniere
che si die tenir per tenger panni per larte maggiore.

Piece dyeing from Rosetti's work
Plictho de Larte de Tentori.

Arsenic appears fairly often in recipes from older times and its purpose can, as in these instructions, be multiple. Arsenic can thus promote fixing of alumina mordant (alum) on the fiber material, and it dissolves easily in warm water, making the bath react mildly acidic. Through its affinity to vegetable and animal matter it has a favorable effect on wool and silk fibers that keep a higher gloss by this method. In all this, arsenic does what the dyers call beautification, that is it gives the fiber a greater chroma and brilliance.

The bran that is used in the bath should be for the purpose of making the dye liquid acidic, which is favorable in kermes dyeing in the same manner as in the similar cochineal dyeing. (See comments on page 176.)

In the instructions, the word "boiling" is used in several places in the text. Apparently it has to do with a less rich vocabulary in the transcript of the original formula. Each dyer knows that such a high temperature during so many stages will damage the strength and gloss of the fabric, and thereby also the color. With red dyeing in particular, a temperature of 70-90°C, is not only sufficient, but preferable.

Kermes – *Coccus* – *Krmi* – *Kirmiz:* Different Times, Different Places, Different Names

The words for kermes that are used in various cultural areas reflect the differences of opinion that have long reigned about whether the kermes dyestuff is an animal or a vegetable product. From the Middle East we find names that show that kermes was clearly associated with the animal kingdom there. In Sanskrit (ancient Indian) the word for grub is *krmi* and in Persian (old Iranian) it is *kerema*. In Turkish and Armenian the word *kirmiz* is used for kermes just as it is for the color red. On the other hand, the Romans and Greeks of antiquity regarded kermes as being of vegetable origin and gave it the Greek word *coccus,* which means berry, always as an added word alluding to the plant world. An example of this is *coccus ilicis* or *coccus uva ursi*, that is kermes from oak and bearberry, respectively.

The Bible mentions kermes using the Hebrew word for grub, *tola* or *tolaat,* often combined with the term *schani* which means bright red. Combined, the word can approximately be translated as scarlet grub.

During the Middle Ages kermes went under the name of *vermiculus* or *vermiculum* (Latin for little grub) and cloth that is dyed with it was called vermiculata. The French word *vermeil* is derived from the Latin word, and was later changed to *vermillion.* The latter expression — which is used for the dyestuff vermillion today — originally referred to the bright red kermes color.

The Decline and End of the Production of Kermes

Although cochineal was already known in Europe during the latter part of the 1500s, kermes kept its position as a leading dyestuff for red colors until the mid-1600s. It is generally thought that the cause of its decline and end is connected to the famous discovery that cochineal treated with tin chloride gave an even more brilliant and shinier red color. But you can ask if that was the real reason behind the decline of the kermes era. A more believable cause could be that cochineal simply made a cheaper and almost technically equal alternative for the dye works. If kermes' cost had been on a level with cochineal, it should have been reasonable to test tin on the dyestuff that had been used for centuries. The chemist Berthollet was no stranger to the idea.

If one considers the differences between the production of carmine dyestuff from both the kermes and the cochineal insects, you realize that kermes, despite being considered to be of a higher quality, could not have competed with cochineal in the long run. Collecting the small kermes scale insects from the leaves of wild host plants or from the roots was an unbelievably time-consuming job. On the other hand, cochineal was easier to handle in size and purpose for regular large-scale breeding on well-protected plantations with good climactic conditions and cheap labor forces.

A long, and in more than one way shining, epoch in the history in the art of dyeing ended when the use of kermes ended.

Polished velvet fragment from Brussa (now Bursa) in Turkey, 1300-1400s. Dyestuff analysis showed that the red colors were dyed with lacdye and the blue with indigo.

Lacca: The Indian Lac Scale Insect

A Centuries' Old Dispute

The learned of antiquity had, as we have recently have seen, divided opinions about where the kermes scale insect belonged biologically. The eastern authors regarded it as part of the animal kingdom, while their western counterparts considered it part of the plant kingdom. As we know, the former were right. Another type of scale insect belongs to the group of dyestuff-producing scale insects that caused debate among experts. Not because they were in doubt about its biological habitat, but because they were unable to determine how this worthwhile red dyestuff was produced and what role the insect itself played in the matter. The source of this many hundred-year-old dispute is the Indian lac scale insect *Tachardia (Laccifer) lacca*, and the expensive dyestuff lac, lac-lacca, or lacdye produced using this insect.

From the highlands of Cashmere.

Area of Origin, Designations, and Host Plants

The lac scale insects are spread over various areas of southern and southeastern Asia. They have been found in many parts of India, as far west as the province of Sind in the long valley of the Indus River, and also in Nepal, Cashmere, Tibet, the far end of India, and Sri Lanka.

The lac scale insect appeared in both wild and cultivated forms. The types that are richest in dyestuff came from countries at the far end of India, including Laos, Burma, and others. These areas are believed to be the oldest production areas for the lac dye. From here, the dyestuff was exported to countries lying to both the east and the west. In a Chinese description from the 300s the imported lac is mentioned as being used in dyeing raw silk among other things.

The word lac appears, according to Donkins earlier quoted work, to be of Cambodian origin, called *le-ak*. In Sanskrit it was written as *lâkshâ*.

The Indian name lac, sometimes spelled laq, means hundreds of thousands, which hints at the enormous amount of insects that were consumed in the production of the dye.

The lac scale insect has various trees as host plants, most of which belong to the Ficuss family *(Ficus indica, F. religiosa)*. In a pharmacy textbook from 1836, it is stated that *Ficus indica* can reach an "unbelievable size and old age." As an example a famous tree by the banks of the holy Narbada (or Nerbudda) River is mentioned, and the tree is believed to be close to 2000 years old!

In January the lac females invade sappy young annual shoots of the fig tree and wait to be fertilized by the males who fly there. To this point the works on entomology and the larger reference books generally agree in their descriptions of life of the life of lac scale insects. It is in the descriptions of the subsequent sequence of events that the various points of view become evident.

In his *Lehrbuch der Chemie*, Jacob Berzelius developed the idea that the plant discharged a milk-like substance as a result of the lac females stinging the thin bark of the tree and that the substance then surrounded the red colored insect and its larva in an increasingly hard coat. Through proper treatment, both the lacdye-dyestuff and a worthwhile lac preparation (shellac) could be derived. Berzelius' thoughts have since been more or less repeated verbatim in many technical writings and reference books.

Another opinion was that the enclosed layer was of a strictly animal nature formed by thin layers of tightly packed female lac scale insects, their larva, and secretions, covering all of the outer branches and twigs of the host plant with a hard red shell.

More modern research reveals that the latter opinion was correct to the extent that the coating in question was not the result of an outflow of a plant caused by an insect sting. Instead the coating was formed by a secretion that came from the insect itself, with the resin component originating from a plant sap taken in by the insect. This sap was passed through the digestive system of the lac scale insect before it was excreted with the secretion from special glands.

Fragment of a Mongolian rug, probably from northwestern India, dated to the mid-1600s. The realistically portrayed plant motif is characteristic of the Mongul Empire. Analysis showed that the deep red color tones were produced with lacdye.

The side brocade, detail of a mass hook from Florence, 1400s. Dyestuff analysis showed that the red color was dyed with lacdye.

Collection of Lacdye Dyestuff

Several months after the lac female was fertilized, the coat surrounding it became 3-8 mm thick, and in some places it was several centimeters thick. By then the fig tree had become an increasingly beautiful red color and the "harvest" of lac and dyestuff could begin.

The branches and twigs surrounding this shell were removed from the tree and broken into smaller pieces of about ten cm in length. These were then placed in the sun to dry and kill the insects. The pieces had a yellowish red to dark brown embossed and finely punctured surface which easily break into shiny fractures. In trade these pieces were called stocklac (from the English *sticklack*) *Lacca in ramnlis* or *L. in baculis*, and dyers preferred dark brown Siamese stocklac, which was richer in dyestuff than the yellowish red Bengali "stocklac."

Extraction of Dyes

The products obtained by processing stocklac were the dyestuff and the equally valuable lac. These were separated by first by pounding hard on the material and removing the stalks and woody parts. The residue was crushed to powder which, after being mixed with water, was "reworked" in large troughs using their feet. The resulting red liquid was separated from the resin by decanting and standing untouched as the dyestuff precipitated to the bottom of the trough. After pressing out the remaining water, the dyestuff was shaped into small, bluish black or dark red blocks or cakes.

The resin released from the dyestuff was melted and pressed between banana leaves into thin yellow or brown slices. They were sold as rubber varnish or shellack.

Up to about 6.5 percent of the raw lac was dyestuff, while the purified product contained between 50-80 percent pure lacdye-dyestuff, the so-called laccain acid.

Lacdye is closely related to cochineal's dyestuff, which it sometimes replaces or combines with. One old handbook about dyeing techniques has the following to say. "The color obtained from lac is very genuine, but not as fiery and clear as the one obtained from the cochineal. Therefore a product dyed with lac can be treated for a while afterward in a cochineal bath by which both a fiery and very genuine color is obtained."

The Lac Dyestuff in Textile Cultures:
An Incomplete Account

The lac dye was known and used in India for centuries before it was finally exported to England in 1796. The information comes from *Neues Englisches Färbebuch* published in 1817 by the versatile dye chemist, doctor, and philosopher Edward Bancroft. Some years later it was also introduced it to North America where it became a valued dyestuff during the following century. Its popularity can be attributed to its good fastness and its relatively low price (approximately half of the cost of cochineal), and it eventually replaced cochineal.

We know extremely little about how and for which types of work the lac dye was used in the textile cultures. Western sources are, to say the least, lacking in information, while the Asian cultural folk literary treasures are difficult to obtain or closed to us.

In his work about the rugs of the world, David Black mentions that lac was used in Indian rugs from 1600-1890, mainly during the Mongul Empire and in Persian rug art up to 1850. Lac dyestuff imported from India was used in Egyptian rugs during the Mamluk and Osmask dynasties, 1550-1650. Helmut Schweppe mentions the use of lac in rugs produced in Persia and Turkmenistan. For the time being we will have to be satisfied with this abbreviated information about the use of the lac dye within the textile field, although we have reason to assume that it played a significantly greater role than the meager accounts lead us to believe.

CHU: The Chinese symbol for red

The Chinese dynasties are often associated with one special color: Ming with blue, the Han dynasty with black, and so on. Throughout history red has been the most used of all colors. The old version of the Chinese symbol CHU— one of the symbols that means red — consists of the symbol for a tree where the middle of the trunk is marked by a large point (later by a dash). From this historians have concluded that the original was a red dyestuff extracted from a tree. However there is one catch to this hypothesis. Practically all the colors that are extracted from so-called color trees possess extremely low use fastness. Considering that the Chinese had strict requirements for all types of dyestuffs early on, it is not likely that one color from a color tree has influenced the shape of the symbol. Which other factors may have played a role in the origin of the symbol? Two causes, not unrelated, are possible. First the meaning of the great fig tree itself, completely covered with the red lac secretion out to the outermost tips of the twigs. The sight of this could have played a role in the design of the CHU-character, probably because it was possible to derive one of the red textile dyestuffs with the greatest chroma and durability known to man from that substance. If you interpret the design from this point of view, the clearly marked point on the trunk may symbolize the actual insect that was the source of that valuable substance.

MADDER

Pages from L. Fuchs flora, *printed in Basel in 1545. The drawings show wild and cultivated madder.*

Domácý Mařena. Rubia domeſtica.
1. Gahody. 1. Bacca.
2. Semeno. 2. Semen.

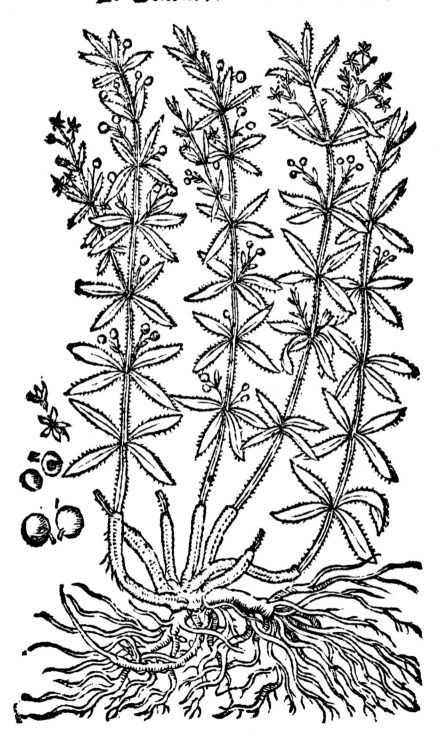

"Red is a Pleasant and Delightful Color."

— Johan Linder, 1720

The Universal Madder Color Plant

The red colors described up to this point have all been of animal origin. They have also all had good fastness and dyeing qualities, but the job of extracting their dyestuff has often been difficult, as we have seen. The purple mollusks had to be collected from cliffs and reefs on the bottom of the sea, the color scale insect from thorny bushes, grass, or root systems. In addition, all of them only existed within more or less limited geographic areas.

A large amount of red to reddish dyestuff can also be extracted from vegetable sources, but despite the high and brilliant tones, these colors possessed, for the most part, very unsatisfactory use fastness. The exception and the blue indigo's coloristic antipode and its complement are made from dyes from this significant group of madder dye plants.

Unlike the indigo plants that belong to completely different families but all contain the same dyestuff, the madder plants all belong to the *Rubicae* family but contain a number of various (although related) red to yellowish red dyestuffs. The plants exist practically all over the whole world in both wild and cultivated forms. They are relatively easy to harvest and need little treatment to make them useable for textile dyeing.

As a dyestuff for wool and silk, the various madder-producing plants are known for producing a rich scale of red, orange, pink, brownish-violet, and brown colors without great difficulty. On the other hand, other vegetable fibers were harder to apply, and the attempt to satisfactorily dye cotton materials, a strong red color, for example, gradually led what may be the most complicated dyeing method known to man, the so-called Turkey red dyeing.

Madder plant (cultivated form); woodcut from 1596.

Madder Dyeing in Early Cultures

Next to indigo, madder was the most used dyestuff in ancient times. Many scientific investigations and antique sources document this fact. When he analyzed a belt from Tutankhamun's grave (died 1350 BC), the English textile researcher quoted earlier in this work, Pfister, found that it was dyed with madder and that the same dyestuff was also used on a woven fabric from the 18th dynasty (1500-1350 BC). In both cases the fastness of the dye was low, which allowed him to conclude that, unlike their Indian colleagues, Egyptian dyers at that time had not yet satisfactorily mastered the technique of mordanting a cellulose fiber material with a madder dye.

The methods of analysis available to modern textile researchers have confirmed earlier assumptions and uncovered unexpected conditions. Pfister, who analyzed a number of the dyes that were known at the beginning of our chronology, found that the dyestuff that was most highly prized in former times, mollusk purple, was completely lacking in fragments of Egyptian material. He found that purple's coloristic counterpart was always produced by combining a red dyestuff, most often madder, with a blue, always woad-indigo.

Recent reports from China about several sensational archeological grave finds reveal the country's formerly known sources of dyeing and printing on fabric in a unique manner. In contrast to what is usually the case, the material consists of extremely well-preserved, entire costumes and woven fabrics from about a half a century before to a couple of thousand years after the beginning of our chronology. The burial find shows that the main dyestuffs were madder for red, indigo for blue, and gardenia for yellow colors. Noteworthy is the intense light fastness and the well-preserved strong coloring of the madder dyes, indicating good saturation of the fibers and a carefully selected mordanting process. Various written sources remind us of the high dyeing technological standards in old China. In the oldest Chinese reference work ERH-YA they speak of a dyeing process in three different steps, which we can translate to the pre-treatment of the fiber material through washing and bleaching, its mordanting with appropriate metal salts, and finally the handling of the textile material in one or more dye baths.

Investigations of South American textiles have also given unexpected results. The red colors have not, as has long been assumed, mainly been dyed with carmine acid from the domestic cochineal scale insect. Margareta Ekroth-Edebo, who did dye analyses on several of my own textile fragments, has also tested the red dyes in ten items from the Peruvian textile collection at Göteborg's Ethnographic Museum. They are from pre-Columbian times and represent three cultures, limited in time and in stylistic aspects: Paracas 900-200 B.C., Nasca 200 B.C. - 600 A.D., and Pachacamac in the centuries around the year 1000.

All red nuances of the yarns in Paracas articles turned out to be dyed with a domestic madder plant of the *Relbunium* family while all the red and many brown and bluish black shades in the more recent textiles were produced with cochineal. In a large 1986 study, UCLA Professor M. Saltzman examined 141 samples from Paracas textiles, and only three were dyed with cochineal, while the others were dyed with *Relbunium*.

Almost twenty-five members of the *Relbunium*-family are native to South America and several are suitable for dyeing textiles. The dye-giving substances are purpurin and pseudo purpurin, while the alizarin in *R. tinctorum* is lacking in all types.

Dyeing of Madder in the Literature of Antiquity

Many older authors tell about the early use of madder. The Greek author Herodotus, whom Cicero once gave the honorary title "the father of history," describes how he himself witnessed the use of madder during a trip that he took to Egypt in 450 BC. Pliny also knew the dye and the plant from which the dyestuff was extracted. He called it *Rubia* and in book XIX of his *Historia Naturalis*, he correctly describes the use of the roots for dyeing. The plant he describes corresponds well with the one that would become known as *Rubia tinctorum* some centuries later. In his text about it he continues: "The first of these is Rubia, the use of which is necessary in dyeing wool and leather. The Italian type is the most valued and in particular that which grows in the areas around the city Rome. Nearly all of our provinces also produce it in great quantities. It grows wild, but is suitable for cultivation. . ."

The presence of madder is noted from the costal areas of west to southwest Asia Minor. Based on his travels the Emperor Claudius' physician Dioscorides reported that it was cultivated in the province of Cyrene, and the geographer Strabo (born around 63 B.C.) gives us the following picture in his work *Geografica*, the seventeen volumes of which are for the most part still preserved. "The water here in Hierapolis (Lydia) is excellently suited for wool dyeing, so that the material dyed using the root resembles those that were dyed with purple or kermes."

As a result of its common use at that time, madder was simply called "the root" in the Greek writings.

Rubia tinctorum and Other Madder Plants

As was pointed out in the introductory section, the *Rubicae* family includes many types of madder plants. However the word madder is generally used today as a common term when referring to some of these types that vary a great deal among themselves.

Rubia tinctorum is the madder plant that we probably know best and on which the most scientific studies and analyses have been done. It grows wild over practically the entire globe, but has long been cultivated in Europe, Asia, and America. The plant is herblike with soft stalks that easily grow near fields. The lancet like leaves are wreath shaped and the flowers are in bunches. The roots grow horizontally and are fairly small, seldom more than one-half to one cm in diameter, although they can be found up to 60 cm long.

The roots of the cultivated madder make up to four percent of the plant's total weight, a majority among related dyestuffs, primarily alizarin, purpurin and pseudo purpurin. The latter is converted to purpurin by the heat produced during the dyeing process. However, the pseudo purpurin is of great importance because it has the most brilliant of the madder dyestuffs, and the instruction often repeated in the literature — that madder must be dyed at a low temperature (below 70°C) — probably has something to do with that. The reason that pseudo purpurin is not mentioned in older analyses of plant or textile materials may be because it is confused with purpurin by careless analysis.

If this explanation is accepted, it is necessary to keep in mind that if one wants to obtain the most brilliant colors possible using plants of the madder family, the dyestuff should never be subject to temperatures higher than 70°C, whether when drying the roots, (see page 82), during extraction of the dyestuff in the bath (over boiling), in dyeing, or during treatment afterwards.

It also seems as if pseudo purpurin to a higher degree should dominate in certain *Galium*-types, which should explain why these are sometimes are preferred to the cultivated madder. Grazing animals easily absorb madder dyestuff into their body secretions such as urine and milk. The dye also bonds to the calcium in bones, turning their skeletons red.

There are several other *Rubia*-types that had great economic and practical significance in olden times. We find their sophisticated rose tones and intense red colors on Oriental textiles of various kinds: rugs, embroidery and calico prints. To put together a short and correct account of these textiles is hardly possible, partly because their numbers are so great and partly because accessible sources regarding naming, areas of origin, and dyestuff content are so scattered. Therefore I have chosen to select the compilation here from *Colour Index*, created by The Society of Dyers and Colourists, Bradford, 1971. This work which is regarded as the most comprehensive and exhaustive encyclopedia of natural and synthetic textile dyestuff. Some additional data of a more historical nature has been added to these reports.

A strong brilliant red color was formerly derived from the madder plant cultivated in the East Indies *Munjeet* (or Indian madder), *Rubia cordifolia* and *R. khasnia,* to give an even deeper color tone.

For calico print production, the root of *Oldenlandia umbellata,* which grows in sandy fields in India, Sri Lanka, and Burma, was used. It primarily contains the same dyestuff as normal madder, but is considered to give a more brilliant red color. Previously, it could be purchased in dried bundles on the Indian markets under the name of *Chadar* or *Chaia.* Before they were put into the dye bath, *Chaia*-roots had to be finely pulverized, pestling it in a stone mortar (a wooden mortar was considered completely unsuitable) with the careful addition of "hard" (calcium containing) water.

The root of "hirda," *Terminalia chebula,* could also be used for calicoes. Due to its high tin content it was especially suitable for black colors and in "gallering" (tanning material) of cotton cloths in Turkey red dyeing or printing.

Other than indigo, few dyestuffs from the plant kingdom can be dyed in cold baths. One of them comes from the root of *Morinda citrifolia,* which is cultivated in certain parts of India and which gives a strong red color without having to heat the dye bath. In 1775 Carl Peter Thunberg, also called the Linné of Japan, wrote the following from Batavia: "Morinda citrifolia is called Bengado and the sap of the root was used by the Javanese to dye red. . ."

Another *Morinda*-type that became particularly significant for wax batik manufacture came from the root bark of a bush, *Morinda umbellata.* It is used on Java for its durable red color, but also in certain areas of India and on Sri Lanka.

In the Nordic countries the roots of various types of bedstraw were once used. The white bedstraw, *Galium boreale,* which was already known in Viking times, is an example. Wool was dyed red using alum. In East Bothnia, in Finland, white bedstraw was called *"mattara."*

Another previously used bedstraw, particularly on Öland and Gotland, was the dye bedstraw, *Galium triandrum (Asperula tinctoria),* which was also used to dye wool red.

VITMÅRA, GALIUM BOREALE L.

The white bedstraw, Galium boreale. *From Svensk botanik, 1802-1806.*

The Cultivation, Harvest, and Preparation of Madder

Factors such as the type of cultivation, soil, and climate conditions all influence the quality of the madder and the quality of the dyestuff. Thus the older, cultivated plants in limy soil give greater color yield than the younger ones grown in lime-poor fields.

Large-scale cultivation of madder has taken place in Europe ever since the Middle Ages. It first arrived in France through the decree of Charlemagne in the 800s which dealt with a common type of madder (*Rubia tinctorum*), but which later was expanded through smuggling and cultivation of the Turkish variation *Rubia peregrina* to other countries in Europe. A survivor of that "import" is the variety that grows wild in a few places in southwestern England and on the Aran Islands and Ireland.

A kind of madder that was long considered the finest in Europe was cultivated in the suitable clay soil of the Dutch province of Zeeland and used by purchasers for testing incoming supplies of madder. In Vetenskap Akademie's (Science Academy) documents from 1755, there is a detailed account of the Zeelandic cultivation of madder. It was written by Professor Gustaf Lidbeck in Lund who had visited that location, and a few sections from his description will be used here to illustrate some of the steps involved in the processing of the Dutch madder. The text is greatly abbreviated, and is given here in a more readable form.

The soil in Zeeland consists of clay and clay mixed with soil. The areas where the madder will be planted the following spring are plowed deep, and in the winter they are fertilized. In the end of April or the beginning of May, one-, two-, or three-year-old roots and groups of side roots are carefully loosened from the old stem root, which is immediately placed in a basket of dirt and transplanted by placing three young shoots or side roots in a little triangle. A row of these groups is planted along the entire length of the bed, with each and every triangle being one foot apart. These new plants are kept free of weeds, and a small iron rake is used to keep the soil around the roots loose.

In the month of October when the plant becomes more than partially visible (above ground), it is plowed between the rows with a plow that has a high and large turning blade. The earth that covers the area as a result of rain and storms is two to three inches high over the plant itself, which protects the roots from cold and leaves the next year's shoots enough topsoil to shoot out into. In September and October the roots that are two to three years old (because they seldom are in the ground longer) and as thick as a Swan pen are gathered using long, pointy, and slightly bent iron spades. They are immediately thrown into a pile on the field, where they lie for one to two weeks to air out and to allow the air to blow through them.

These roots, from which the stems and leaves are removed when they begin to turn yellow, are placed in a room outside the drying house itself. After four to five days the roots are placed inside the drying house itself, which has been constructed at great expense from stone and with a roof that is approximately 20 "aln" long, 16 wide, and 15 "aln" high (1 aln = about 60 cm). The oven with its vaults goes far into the house and numerous pipes go from all sides of it all the way up the walls. The roots that have to be dried are first laid on the lower bar, after which they are spread thin and lie for a day. Then they are eventually moved higher and higher in the drying house. When the roots have laid in the drying house in this manner for five days, they are moved to a smaller one which is next to it. The roots are laid on a drying bench with slanted sides, that have wool coverings on them and the roots are placed there under high heat for about twelve hours, sometimes somewhat longer, as required.

Then the roots are moved to another room where they are threshed, partly to get all the impure earth and so fourth out of them, partly to loosen the husk, which gives the worst dye (earth madder).

After threshing, the roots are taken to the stamp house where the larger and smaller parts are sorted and separated from each other and then they are placed in a stamp trough fitted with iron plates where they are stamped down. Then the stamped-down pieces are sifted through courser and finer sieves made of calf leather, in a closed and well insulated room so that the fine powder may not fly around and disappear.

When the madder is sorted, it is packed very well and stored for one to two years, then it is better than it is when it comes directly from the stamp trough, and is considered best when it has the shade of the saffron color and gives off a strong but not unpleasant odor.

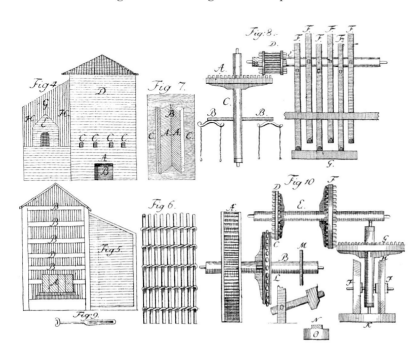

Drying house and stamp work for production of madder, 1787.

About Madder from Outside of Europe

The Levantine or Smyrna madder was considered the best type of madder root introduced to Europe during the 1700s and 1800s. Theese roots were traded in the form of pressed whole pieces, and their unsurpassed quality was ascribed to the high age of the roots, which were allowed to stay in the ground for five to six years before they were harvested. In trade they were called Alizari or Lizzari, and the most important export harbor for them was, as the name indicates, the city of Smyrna.

An author of a dye book from 1772 believed that the high quality and "lively color" of the Smyrna madder was due to the fact that the madder roots were exclusively air dried in the Levantine areas of production before they were pulverized. Thus they were not subjected to what was considered the damaging high heat in warmed up ovens. The author also says that this type of madder, which he called Chioc Boya (Turkish, *kökboya*) in Levantine, was valued much higher than the Zeelandic, which the Dutch exported to there.

Madder Flower, Madder Extract, and Garancin

In addition to alizarin, purpurin, etc., the madder roots contain a large number of elements that have a negative impact on the outcome of a dyeing. With the flowering calico print industry in the 1800s, there was an increased demand for a madder product with greater chroma that was easier to handle. Efforts had long been focused on producing a contaminant-free madder product containing a more concentrated form of the dyestuff. Resulting products included madder flower, madder extract, and Garancin. Madder flower was obtained by soaking the pulverized root in water (or water with an added acid), washing it out, pressing it, drying it and finally grinding the soaked-out product. This preparation certainly gave a more pure color, but it is doubtful if it justified the production costs and work effort.

Madder extract was a common name for a number of preparations that were made from the dyestuff of the madder root treated with various solvents. However there was not a large market for these compounds.

Alizarin is one of the most important dyestuffs of the madder roots. One particular madder product, Garancin, was especially used in the calico print industry. It consisted of a powder preparation with a chroma four to six times higher than the original madder. The Garancin was produced by treating the dried and ground roots with sulfuric acid; the woody roots were destroyed and charred, while the alizarin itself remained unaffected. After this process, the Garancin compound, containing the most useful red madder dyestuff with the greatest chroma, may be considered the product that made it possible to produce the Turkey red calico prints that eventually became so famous.

Coptic fragment from the 400s. The analysis showed that the brown-violet threads only contained dyestuff from madder. No trace of purple or from mixed dyeing with indigo or woad could be found. The violet "purple color" probably has been created by mordanting with iron. The content of iron in the dyed threads was high, compared with the light and undyed sections. The dyed parts were also much more fragile. Iron ions accelerate the breakdown of natural fibers even if the object has been stored in darkness, which is probably the case with this fragment, because the color is still equally strong on the front and back sides.

Madder Forgeries

Just as new shipments of indigo were quality-checked with visual, taste, and smell tests, and finally by dyeing a piece of white felt, madder supplies had to be tested as well. The ground madder was often subject to falsification with the help of brick powder, sand, and dyed sawdust. A test dyeing was a worthwhile step here too.

Madder dyed wool yarns.

What Colors Does Madder Produce?

One of the larger works on the history of dyeing states that "madder has a fresh, yellowish-red tone." Under very special conditions the statement is valid, but as a general rule for indicating color results from a madder dyeing, it is way too weak.

In contrast to synthetically produced dyes, natural dyestuffs are not treated in a uniform manner, and madder is no exception. These dye components go from the more yellowish-red alizarine to the bluish-red purpurin. In addition, these components influence (often unfavorably) the clarity and chroma of the main color to varying degrees. This, combined with a number of other interactive factors during the dyeing process, results in madder not automatically producing one specific color. With madder it is possible to obtain a range of very different colors. In the section about purple and the color scale insect we saw that similar conditions prevailed.

Some of the factors that influenced the color of a madder dyeing will be briefly mentioned here. The type of madder the roots are extracted from and the conditions under which they were cultivated, harvested, etc. (see page 80) are of primary importance. The calcium content of the place where it grows is especially important. Calcium content not only influences the dye yield, but also the depth of the color. In addition the water quality, the temperature of the dye bath, and the pH values also play an important role. The material that the dyeing vessel is made from, such as iron or copper, is also important.

Of greatest significance to the visual appeal of the madder dye is the mordanting substance and methods used.

Thus madder not only comes in a "fresh yellowish red tone" but turns a range of different shades, from orange over strong red to deep brown violet and almost black-brown colors.

Old Madder Formulas

"To dye wool and cloth a red color"

—G. Rosetti, 1548

"Add 250 g of Roche alum for each kg of wool and let it mordant for 1½ hours. Rinse it (the wool) very carefully in pure water. After it is well washed, calculate 250 g of madder for each kg of wool, which will be allowed to boil in pure water. Add the madder in the water when it is just ready to boil, then the wool, and let it boil hard for ½ hour. After washing, a good color is obtained - it is red."

Commentary

Two things are of special interest here. The mordanting bath does not contain any wine stone, but only alum, and Rosetti recommends a thorough rinsing of the mordanted wool, which eliminates the weak acid formed in the fiber material through alum mordanting and a deep red color is obtained.

Madder Red on Wool

—"An Genuine and Reliable Dye-Book," 1759

"Take a kettle, add 4 'kannor' of water, 6 'Lod' of Roman Alum, 4 'Lod' of red wine stone, allow the yarn to boil in here for two hours, then take it up and let it cool, add 4 'kannor' of pure water to the kettle, 10 'Lod' of fine madder, let it warm up, then add the yarn that was treated with alum and let it work well for 2 hours; but do not let it boil, but keep it good and hot; then take it out, rinse and dry, then it is done."

Commentary

The above recipe comes from one of the earliest published Swedish handbooks on print dyeing and very briefly gives the most important instructions for a basic recipe with madder. The suggested quantity of wine stone may seem unnecessarily large and some rinsing of the product after mordanting is not recommended, which would have been appropriate there. On the other hand it is emphasized that the temperature of the bath should not be too high, but only "kept very hot."

Conversions for the weights and measures used in this recipe:
1 "skålpund," = 425 g. 1 "kanna" = 2.6 liters, 1 "lod" = 13.3 g

Rinsing of dyed goods in the stream outside the dye works often took place from a dyeing bridge or as here, from a boat. The copperplate is from a work about dyeing by P.J. Macquer, 1759.

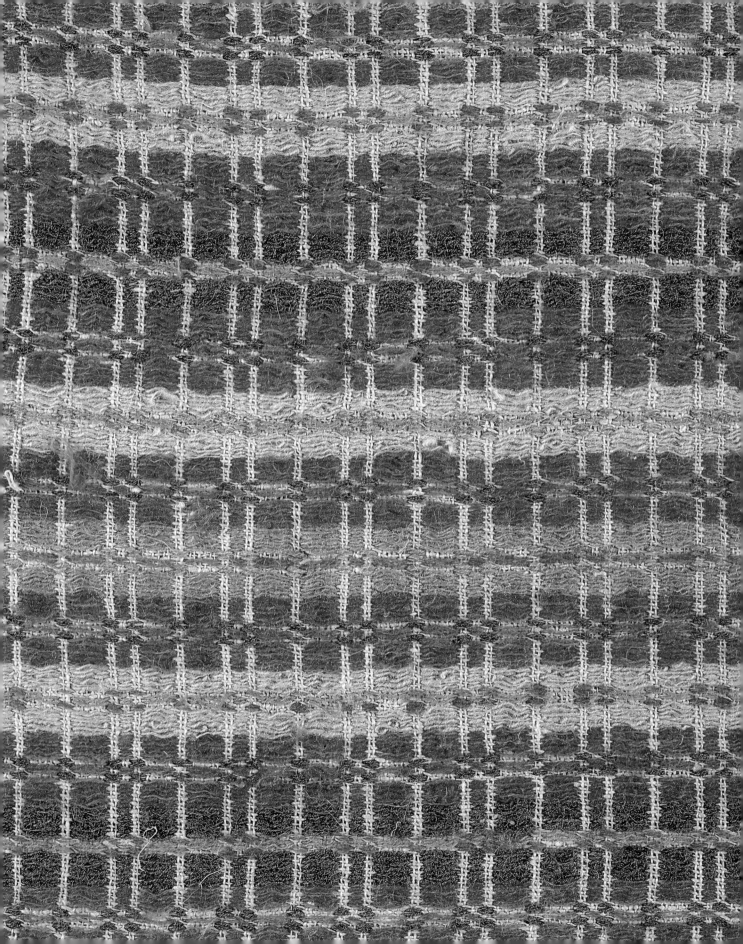

Decorative scarf from Lits parish, Jämtland, the pattern from plangi - or tie-dyeing technique. Dated to the late 1700s.

Dyeing with Madder in Folk Textile Art

If the blue color is associated with the ancient Nordic God Odin's cloak, the Celtic prince's costumes, or the French heretic's clothing dyed with woad, the red color of madder is similarly associated with the diversified textile products of the Middle East. In rugs, woven fabrics, and textile prints, madder has been the dominant color throughout time. To describe madder's use in various times and cultures in a limited space seems to be an equally meaningless and impossible task, so I have chosen instead to give a few selected, detailed examples.

"About the Land Turkomania"

The part of Asia Minor that previously went under the name of Anatolia — today Turkey — has for thousands of years been considered one of the origin areas of folk rug art. The adventurous travelers who journeyed through these areas in the 1200 and 1300s (Vilhelm of Rubruk, Ibn Battuta), and others give very little rug information. The situation is very different in the account by their contemporary, Marco Polo, from the city of Koicula. That Marco was from a family that had worked with textiles for generations is often obvious from his texts, in

Opposite page: Weaving in a "monk belt" from Dalarna. The wool yarn in the red portions is dyed with madder.

87

The fragment is a kelim weave from Anatolia. Several hundred years ago this kelim was woven by a Turkman woman from a city in the area of Adana and Maras in the Taurus Mountains, where her tribe had its summer camp. The rhombuses with cross divisions and the diagonal color positioning are universal, but are usually part of shamanic symbols, such as the middle of a larger polygon. The figure that fills out the area between the cross-divided fields is probably a stylization of a significantly more intricate pattern of a horned animal, a human, or a combination of both. Horned shamans are found reproduced on ceramics from Hacilar 5,500 years before the beginning of our chronology. Male animals, horses, and rams were offered to ancient Nordic Gods to ensure the balance of nature and the balance between heaven and earth. In woven fabrics they were symbolized by the colors blue and red. For the most part the border is gone, but the part that remains shows a bird border with an eagle or double eagle. These powerful birds were often used in kelims to ward off evil forces and take away the center of the kelim, where the good, holy, and fertility-promoting symbols were placed. The border pattern thus served as a magic barrier. After the discovery of the Anatolic 8,500-year-old portrait of the city, Çatal Hüyük, there has been much discussion about the exposed murals found there were reproductions of early kelim weavings or if kelims from later times were inspired by the Neolithic paintings instead. Regardless of who inspired whom, we can ascertain that the Turkman women have kept an ancient tradition for making patterns with all of their magical symbols, colors, and language of form alive for thousands of years, right up to our times.

particular his account "About the land of Turkomania." He relates the following about the rug-weaving, nomadic people.

"They live in the mountains and in inaccessible places, where they find good pasturage for their herds, which they simply live for. . . Here the best and most beautiful rugs and silk materials in carmine and other wonderful colors are woven."

A modern traveler who is also acquainted with the lives of the Turkmen nomadic people, their thoughts, and especially with their rug weaving skills is textile researcher Sonny Berntsson. His well-informed descriptions show that conditions have not changed remarkably in the 700 years that have passed since Marco Polo visited. He paints a collective image of a people that have to move with their herds to the places where the pasturage is good: up in the mountains in the summer and down in the lowlands in the winter.

As a rule they live in tents made from goat hair or felted wool, depending on the climate zone. For practical reasons they have no furniture of the type we use, and they make sacks, bags, etc., to store their possessions. They also produce textiles that are necessary for practical life, including tent strings, blankets, etc. Both pile and flat carpets make up an important part of the production and are used as floor coverings to sit or lie on, as well as insulation. The bags and rugs were made of wool and goat hair from their own animals.

The women were responsible for this significant part of the nomadic people's lives. Over centuries they developed their technical knowledge — spinning, dyeing and weaving — and refined their ability to create patterns. As an inheritance from mother to daughter this art has lived on and gone forth.

Every woman regarded weaving and rug tying as a free time occupation where she could express her creative ability and artistic talent. It also gave her an opportunity to gain great respect from her neighbors by decorating her home or tent with beautiful utilitarian textiles and rugs, giving the family high status.

It is often possible to trace the origins of the symbols and decorative elements in the traditional inheritance patterns used in these rugs and utilitarian textiles to pre-Islamic times, when the people's religion embraced a shamanic view of the world. (See the patterns on pages 90 and 93.)

The picture shows the patterned side of a Çuval, *a storage sack that nomads and half-nomads in southern Anatolia previously kept wool, clothing, and other textiles in. The patterned side of the sack is always turned toward the room or the tent. A broad, single-colored section divided the two patterned fields, which should be viewed vertically. The Çuval gave the home or the inside of the goat hair tent a varied and decorative look, while its pattern also had a strong symbolic meaning. The main motif is divided with a cross with a definite center, göbek (=navel), which is the center of the heavens, with the four points of the compass repeated in a motif that seems infinite, a multi-universe. This pattern was considered to be in touch with the cosmic forces and had the ability to give a high pro-creative power. Part of this concept of the world lives on with the older nomadic women, who experience the energy of the heavens and the matter of the Earth meeting in a divine union. This Çuval is from the areas around Adana and Marash in southern Anatolia. It was woven sometime between 1825 and 1850 in areas where stock-raising nomads (yörüks) still lived in a completely tradition-bound life style. A yörük family owned several thousand sheep and goats with which they wandered through high and low lands according to the changing of the seasons.*

The colors of the storage sack have very old-fashioned nuances of warm red from madder (kökboya) and bluish red, probably from kermes, which Armenian dyers offered for sale in these regions. In addition, a deep indigo blue color and the white of undyed cotton have been used. The aubergine blue color found in woven fabric from this time period was reportedly dyed with a mixture of indigo, madder, and tanning material from gall nuts, via a method that has been forgotten today.

Sonny Berntsson

The Signs of the Red Earth

Asiatic textile folk art has shown a love for red and the blue colors since pre-Islamic times. Together with other shamanic base elements, red and blue make up the elements that both separate and unite heaven and earth.

In felt works from Kazakhstan and in kelims and folk pile carpets from the Middle East, you can experience the significance of the red and the blue colors right up to our own times.

In the older conception of the world, the powers of the blue heavens and the red of the earth united to create life, a sort of cosmic marriage. Another textile pattern design that forms this relationship is the shoulder that unites heaven and earth, the cosmic shoulder or world's tree. The colors blue and red are used there too, and they symbolize the greatness of father/mother, spirit/matter. The human relationship to the red color is loaded with symbolism and events. Through grave finds we know that ochre has been strewn over the dead body. The red color was life giving in the same way as blood. Even skeletons and craniums were strewn with the red ochre color.

Rug weaver from a town near Pamukkale, Taurus Mountains, Anatolia.

Turkman woman grinding grain. In the background the storage bags with kelim patterns on some parts.

Pictures of the midwife — the great mother — are found as statues or reliefs modeled in red brown clay. The surfaces have been painted with red ochre in magical patterns: concentric circles, rhombi, and zigzag lines. Such an example is this eight thousand-year-old midwife from the Neolithic high culture's Çatal Hüyük in Anatolia. There she was worshiped for her life-giving powers both in birth and death cults. She is shaped in red clay and painted with magical patterns in red ochre. The red color is her attribute, and the color accompanies all later fertility goddesses, including Kybele, Isis, and Artemis, where sacrificial blood runs in rivers in their honor. The red sacrificial blood has always had strong influence on people in the older centuries. Originally Oriental women would dip the palms of their hands in the sacrificial blood that had absorbed the powers of the earth, and even today Oriental women paint the palms of their hands with it as a left over from an ancient sacrificial cult.

Red and blue are often primary colors in many Islamic and Asiatic textiles. Even today the interplay between the powers of the red earth and the blue heavens is found in the textile handwork of many Iranian and Turkish tribes. That the root of madder actually grows in the life-giving earth strengthens this power even more.

Bride's sack Gelinçuvali *(detail of the front side), Turkey. This storage sack was an important part of a nomadic woman's property. In it she kept her own clothing, including her bridal clothing and other valuable possessions. The back of the bridal sack has beautiful edging in indigo blue, madder red and brownish yellow colors. Braided goat hair bands around the outer sack edges made it easier to handle when moving between winter and summer work.*

The sack was made sometime during the second half of the 1800s in northwestern Anatolia, in the area between Bergama and Balikesir. The Turkmen woman who wove it has preserved the tribe's many hundred year old pattern tradition well. Above all, the patterns on these bridal sacks symbolized power. The women themselves say that these patterns give them ugur *(luck),* saglik *(freshness), and* yavsam *(vitality).*

A bridal sack was inherited and used for several generations and many middle aged women can tell that their sack was woven by their great-grandmother.

The bridal sack pictured here was woven using two techniques, the patterned portions in "tuskaft" (reps) and the patterned field in "soumak" technique .

The mother of Dorgé the dyer spins wool on the steps of her home in Lazaropole near the Macedonian-Albanian border.

The cuff of a sleeve of a hand-woven coarse linen cloth embroidered with symbols in chain seams of hard-wined, madder-dyed wool yarn. The cuff was part of a woman's wedding costume from the Prilep area in southern Macedonia.

Folk Embroidery Art in Macedonia

"In her embroidery she raised herself to the heights of her art and in it she placed all the riches of her soul. . . " These words are those of Maritza Popstefanievas, the untiring researcher and enlightening portrayer of Slavic embroidery art, discussing the ornamentation of the Macedonian women's clothing. Those who have participated in the festivities that surround a Macedonian wedding, and enjoying the red costumes against a background of dull drums and flute-like tones, mixed with the clatter of rows of the Arabian silver coins on the chest, carry forever the image of a singular experience of beauty and the sense that they have participated in something that is more than just outward decor.

For thousands of years the art of embroidery was the Macedonian woman's most popular occupation, to which she applied herself from early childhood and during her entire adolescence. But embroidery was not just a plain form of handwork. In the home, the young girl received comprehensive and methodical instruction accord-

Detail of an embroidery on the lower edge of a woman's shift. Tightly-twined , madder-dyed wool yarn on a linen background. From the Prilep area in southern Macedonia.

ing to a fixed plan so she could gain the necessary skills. To be able to embroider well was considered a qualification, but the one who could compose new ornaments gained even greater admiration and a higher status in her region.

The development and the artistically high level of the art of embroidery depends on several different factors. Above all climate and farming conditions make it possible to produce textile's raw materials — flax, hemp, wool, and silk. For the dyeing itself, the accessibility of domestic plants including various types of madder and mordant minerals was of great importance. Geography naturally plays an important role in pattern formation and the cut of the garment. Macedonia lies in the middle of the Balkan peninsula — the bridge between East and West — and has always been an important link and arena for various people and cultural currents. The embroidered ornament of the clothing naturally reflects all of these foreign influences, but they have been assimilated and given a strong, amalgamated form and a national folk originality and character.

Slavic, Byzantine, and Turkish Influences

Although it is known that southern Slavic people came to the Balkan peninsula and probably had their clothing decorated with multicolored embroidery, circumstances surrounding their arrival and culture have been investigated to an insignificant degree. The Greek historian Priscus (400s) relates that in the court of Attila, the king of the Huns (on the lower Danube) the Slavic women and Attila's wife embroidered multicolored embroideries on linen weave for their clothing.

The lavish design of the Byzantine clothing and brownish black embroideries on the Coptic tunics were also reflected in the Macedonian costumes. The Turks' arrival to Balkan in the 1200s brought an eastern influence that finally replaced the Byzantine influence. In many respects the Turks imposed Oriental culture on Macedonian society as a whole, but the original structure of the farming population remained basically unchanged. This was also true of their clothing customs. While the clothing of the city people was strongly influenced by the Turks, the country dress, particularly that of the women, remained completely unchanged. Despite centuries of influence from various directions, these mountain people have preserved the ancient and distinctive character of their traditional clothing, dances, and songs into recent times.

Conversation at the loom. The city of Zavoj in the area of Lake Ohrid in southern Macedonia.

The Color and Form of the Embroidery Patterns

Macedonian embroidery patterns are predominantly geometric. The forms, plants, and animal motifs which once served as a prototype and inspiration can not be identified today. Many motifs have also had a symbolic and magic purpose, but over time their meaning has been forgotten and the ornament lives on only as decoration.

The main colors of the embroidery are the madder red colors, sometimes combined with a more bluish tone from kermes or cochineal placed against a black or blackish brown color. While embroidery in the young women's clothing has a predominantly light red tone, the embroidery in older women's clothing is of dark and saturated tones. Written descriptions from diplomats and travelers who visited the Turkish empire from as far back as the 1500s describe the rich ornamentation and the red color tones of Macedonian women's clothing.

The Land of the Macedonians

The textile handwork in Slavic and East European areas is often associated with the red madder color. Perhaps this is most clearly experienced in the Balkan Republic of Macedonia, where madder red is found on most textile products, and has its most famous function in the embroidery of the women's clothing.

The republic is named after the Macedonians, a people of unknown origin who lived here before they were pushed aside and mixed with Slavs, Bulgarians, and other peoples. The country borders on Albania in the west, Bulgaria in the east, and Greece to the south. For the most part the land is mountainous, with countless isolated but heavily populated valleys where the climate is so favorable that it is possible to raise tobacco and grapes as well as cotton and rice.

In ancient times Macedonia was part of the kingdom of Alexander the Great, which was eventually expanded to the greatest empire antiquity ever knew. In addition to the Balkan, it included Lydia, Persian Central Asia, and India all the way to Punjabi.

After having been an independent empire, Macedonia came under Turkish rule in the year 1400, which lasted for more than five hundred years, during which time it was a province among many others.

After the second world war it became a partial republic in Yugoslavia, but today it is an independent republic with Skopje as its capital.

Detail of the back of a head covering, Sokai from Bitola, southern Macedonia. The hemp fabric bottom is completely covered with silk and wool embroidery, which creates the impression of woven cloth. Dyestuff analysis showed that the red tones were dyed with madder and cochineal while the blue and green threads gave positive indigo reactions, that is, they were dyed with either woad or indigo.

The little mountain town of Galicnik with its nearly 2,000 inhabitants is known for its beautiful and age-old red costumes.

The town of Zavoj near the Lake Ohrid in southern Macedonia.

Silk	Flax	Wool	Cotton

Madder on Cotton and Other Vegetable Fibers

It is as complicated to dye vegetable fibers like cotton, flax, or hemp with a madder dyestuff as it is uncomplicated to dye an animal fiber with a madder dyestuff. With only alum as a mordant, wool fiber can be dyed a red color that is hearty and has good chroma, and by varying the pH of the dye bath it is possible to manipulate the color toward a yellowish or a bluish color. (See page 84.)

On the other hand, dyeing cotton fiber is not so easy. Just like vegetable fibers, cotton has little or no ability — without very special steps — to stably bond as dyestuff to itself. This explains the almost total absence of recipe instructions for madder dyeing of cotton and flax in the majority of the older dyeing handbooks. The dyeing of wool is described in more or less full detail already when our chronology began. But how and where were the red yarns and materials that reached the western countries from time to time produced?

Textile fragments of madder-dyed and patterned cotton found in archeological digs from Egypt and other places all point to the same area of origin. The textile products that were imported to Europe after the Portuguese discovered the seaway to India and the formation of the East India Company were given names that also hinted at the areas where they were produced. During the 1600s we found the deducible name India red, or genuine Indian red and in 1747 the Adrianopel red (named for Adrianopel in the Middle East, now Edirne) was mentioned for the first time. That same year we also find the color name which more than any other came to be associated with madder dyeing on cotton material: Turkey red, or genuine Turkey red.

Cloth woven from four different types of fibers — silk, flax, wool, and cotton — which were dyed in pieces in medium-strong madder baths. Each type of fiber in three mordant forms: no mordant, alum, tannin, and copper mordant. A dye bath thus resulted in twelve different color nuances.

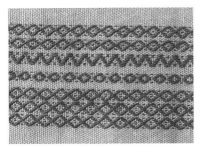

Woven cloth from two types of fibers, wool and cotton. Dyed in medium-strong madder bath.

Opposite page: Detail of the Tunisian cloak. The material is wool and cotton which after weaving is dyed in a madder bath by which the cotton did not absorb any color looks white against the red wool background.

Detail of old Javanese batik, made using a tjanting. Analysis showed that the red color contained "pure alizarin" (from a madder plant).

"Turkey Red: The Greatest of All Dyeing Arts"

From the name, one can be led to believe that the dyeing method originated in Turkey, but it is more likely that the technique came from and was developed somewhere in eastern India. From there it spread through Persia, Armenia, and Syria to Turkey thousands of years ago. From the middle of the 1600s to the beginning of the 1700s, the majority of the dye works for Turkey red dyeing were situated in those areas and in Greece, particularly in the province of Thessaly. Through trading with the Turks, the Greeks had a long-time monopoly on the trading of red-dyed cotton products. It was primarily the French trade houses that purchased and resold these dyed "Oriental" products. The volume of this trade increased steadily right up to the year 1747 when everything was radically changed in one fell swoop.

In a handbook for dyers and printers, *Cours élémentaire de tienture et sur l'Art d'imprimer les toiles* from 1824, written by the priest and chemist J.B. Vitalus, we can participate in the dramatic events that at the beginning of 1747 would thoroughly change the history of dyeing. "That year misters Fraquet, Gouhard, and d'Haristoy started

Fragment of the double ikat woven fabric from the town of Tenganan on the island of Bali. In older times blood was used in connection with madder dyeing. The iron content of the blood may have had a darkening effect on the red color. Later ikat weaves, where blood was not used, have significantly clearer red tones.

two dye works for Turkey red dyeing with the help of a couple of Greek dyers: one at Darnétal near Rouen and the other at Anbenas in Languedoc. Nine years later, in 1756, another private individual, Falchat, who had long lived in the Ottoman Empire (Turkey) brought a number of professionals from there and started a third business near Lyon for dyeing Adrianopel red.

"However, the foreigners could not keep their method of production secret for long, instead the method began to be applied in other places in France. At first with bad results, but eventually so successfully that some French dye works not only copied the Oriental method, but also surpassed it."

In 1765 a detailed description of the new method was worked out, and it spread, so that from that year the process became commonly known among dyers and new businesses started in both northern and southern France. Within a few decades Turkey red dye works were founded in several countries.

Cloth bleaching in St. Gallen,
Switzerland. Painting from the 1600s.

United Turkey Red Company

By the 1700s there were a large number of textile companies in the Leven River Valley in eastern Scotland. Rivers, with their rapidly flowing water and surrounding broad beaches with large open fields, were a suitable location for bleaching cloth and for building printing and dyeing buildings.

In 1785 the textile manufacturer David Dale and his companion Robert Owen (the utopian socialist and social reformer) convinced the Frenchman Pierre Jacques Papillion from Rouen to teach them the complicated and extremely secret Turkey red dyeing process. The commission for promoting manufacturing in Scotland awarded him a prize for writing down all the details of the dyeing process. However, they were not to make the information public for a certain number of years. During that time Papillion alone was to have the benefit of that secret.

From that beginning a great export trade developed up in the Leven Valley with dyed yarn and printed cotton products that went to various parts of the world, but especially to India, China, South America, the Philippines, and the South Sea Islands. Even though there were other businesses in Great Britain that also produced Turkey red dyed and printed products, the main production seems to have been concentrated in the Leven Valley.

In 1896 the three remaining dyeing businesses joined together to form the United Turkey Red Company. The first world war and competition from new textile industries in India and Japan, as well as the introduction of new dyestuffs, lead to a rapid decline for the industry, and the company closed in 1939.

A unique collection of order books with pattern samples from the three companies in the Leven Valley is preserved at the Royal Scottish Museum in Edinburgh. Combined, they cover more than fifty thousand samples from the 1830s to the 1930s, and were rescued from oblivion by an incident that occurred only about ten years ago. The books, with all their information and cloth fragments, were in a condition of nearly total collapse at that time, but have since been the object of a comprehensive conservation project by museum experts. The collection will be one of the treasures of textile history when the restoration is complete.

In Germany, both of the dye cities of Barmen and Eberfeldt supplied "genuine Turkey red" cotton yarn to the Scandinavian countries, among other places.

A written document published in Göteborg in 1781 contains a description by the German-born natural scientist Pallas of "The manner of dyeing Turkish yarn, or the Eastern manner, of putting genuine red color on cotton using madder, as it is done in Astrachan (by the Caspian Sea)." Simon Peter Pallas was one of Linnés most esteemed pen pals and the author *of Flora Russica*, among other things.

However, information about the new dyeing method had reached Sweden earlier via its *chargé de'affaires* in Turkey, Edvard Carleson, who had the process recorded. In a sealed envelope with the words "Description of the method of dyeing red according to the Turkish method, which will be preserved at K. Mt. Manufacturcontoir" written on it, he gave the concerned party his notes.

In Stockholm, a number of small dye works had been established for Turkey red dyeing by David Asplund in the 1780s, but by the middle of the 1800s only Wilhelm Röhs's Levanten dye works, which was started outside of Göteborg in 1827, remained.

The dyer. Colored woodcut by Jost Amman (1539-1591).

Turkey Red:
The Masterpiece of the Art of Dyeing

Turkey red is a pure, cultivated representative for mordant dyeing, but also is undoubtedly the most difficult to handle of all of them. The most important stage of the entire process is the repeated handling of the fiber in an emulsion of Tournant oil (rancid olive oil) or another fatty material. Between the various oilings, the cloth or yarn must be dried by hanging it up in special buildings, the so-called hanging or drying towers. Due to the risk of setting yourself on fire from the oil-mixed textile material, the tower was usually located a way off from the dyeing building. This phase of the dyeing process was significantly simplified after the introduction of new oil preparations (known as Turkey red oil) that consisted of castor oil made water soluble by sulfonation with sulfuric acid.

The production of alum. Woodcut, Basel 1556.

No one has proposed a satisfactory explanation for how this oil treatment works. One name for the process, animalization, hints that it had something to do with a chemical breakdown of the cellulose fiber, which should make it more like an animal fiber and thereby more inclined to bond with the madder dyestuff.

Others are of the opinion that the substance is formed when the fat is oxidized or dominates works like a mordant that happens to bind the dyestuff until it is changed to an insoluble form later in the dyeing process. In order for this to take place, the textile material needs to be treated with alum (kalium-aluminum sulfate) and chalk (calcium). Often the material is also subject to "gallering," a treatment with a tanning material (tannin, gall nut, or sumac extract) before the cotton yarn or cloth is dyed with madder or a closely related dyestuff ("krappering"). The various processes can be combined to some degree, but are still, according to all recipes, extremely time-consuming because, as a rule, they have to be repeated several times to obtain the proper color. A dyeing method called "old red" involved between ten and twenty so-called operations and took up to seven weeks. "New red," which was dyed according to a shortened and simplified (through the introduction of "Turk red oil") dyeing process, still took several weeks.

"To Dye Cotton, Adrianopel, or Turkey Red"

—According to the Artist and Beauty Dyer H. Schrader in Hamburg And the Dyer and Chemist Th. Packer in London

The process for dyeing Turkey red naturally changed from the time it was introduced in Rouen in 1747 to 1869, when artificially produced alizarin was introduced to the market. The introduction of a new textile aid and deeper insights in the field of chemistry also facilitated the work and gave better color results. The fact remained, however, that no dyeing process even approached the number of steps or the degree of difficulty involved in dyeing Turkey red. No uniform method was ever developed, and there only appears to have been agreement on certain essential steps. In practice, there were very divided opinions about the value of certain ingredients and steps. Perhaps a slight impression of the difficulties involved many be drawn from the following sharply abbreviated instructions. They are based on and reconstructed from a German and an English red dyers' handbook, printed, respectively, in the years 1833 and 1840.

First Operation

Involves the excessive boiling of the yarn and the cloth using American potash dissolved in pure river water. After treatment the product is removed and rinsed and then dried.

Second Operation

Covers handling of the product in the "dung bath," which is prepared from sheep dung, industrial olive oil (olive oil) and potash, and as much water as necessary to cover the yarn or cloth. This operation is repeated three times with drying in between the last time by tramping the product in the bath.

Third Operation

Involves mordanting the product in a "white bath," which is prepared using the best industrial olive oil and American potash in a wooden vessel. The product is worked here for half a day, after which it is wrung out and dried. This mordanting is done three times with drying in between, the last time through tramping on the product.

Fourth Operation

The mordanted and dried product is placed in a wooden vessel with cold river water where it is allowed to stay over night. The next day it is rinsed some more in the river.

Fifth Operation

"Gallering" (treatment with tanning material) of the yarn or cloth takes place in a copper kettle filled with pure river water, to which the best kind of sumac, and finely pulverized gall nut from Aleppo (Turkey) is added. After half an hour the product is removed, carefully wrung out, and dried.

An olive plant from which the important Tournant oil is extracted, which makes the Turkey red color possible.

Picture of a gall nut. After olive oil, tannin (the tanning material) from ground gall nuts, was one of the most important aids in Turkey red dyeing.

Sixth Operation

Treatment of the product with alum involves the use of a bath with lukewarm river water with alum and potash added. In this mordant the product that was treated with tanning material was tramped down, after which it was allowed to remain in the liquid for twelve hours. It was removed, rinsed and wrung out, and dried in the air for three to four days. Then the alum process was repeated.

Seventh Operation

Involved dyeing the mordanted product with madder, the so-called "maddering." Iron free, finely pulverized chalk and madder dyestuff which had been crushed and softened in warm water were dissolved in a copper kettle of river water. The bath was heated, but not hotter than you could put your hand in. The material was worked for two hours. In this operation it was necessary to watch the temperature very carefully. The first hour the material was treated at 60°C and the following half hour at 90°C and then it was allowed to boil in a controlled manner for a half hour.

Eighth Operation

Intended to make the "maddered" product more clear in color by boiling in river water and adding American potash and green soap whipped into a lather. How long the product was to be left in the clear kettle "must be left to practical experience and your better judgement, so you must carefully observe when the color becomes beautiful and lively. . ."

Ninth Operation

Consists of beautifying the product by treatment with a tin salt solution for about an hour, after which it is removed, wrung out, and treated, as indicated in the following operation.

Tenth and Final Operation

This operation is usually called avivage and involves putting the beautified product into a soap solution of pure river water and Marseille soap (a core soap which contains olive, peanut, and palm core oil) whipped into a lather. It is allowed to work under even boiling for six hours, after which it is rinsed in the river and dried in the shade.

Commentary

The two authors only differ on a couple of points. One has to do with the madder dyestuff, where Packer recommends the Levanten (Lizzary), which he says "leaves an incomparably more beautiful color than the other types of madder," implying the variety of Schrader and other recommended Dutch ones.

For the madder process Packer considers that a certain quantity of "not coagulated sheep blood must be mixed with the water in the dyeing kettle right after the madder is added." The addition of blood, usually ox blood, is found in many madder recipes, but its value is the subject of lively debate. In one place Bertholl also quotes what an authority in the area of dying, Dr. Ure, says about that: ". . . I believe that the use of blood in the madder bath does not serve any purpose whatsoever, and if the dyers' bias did not stand in the way, then it could be left out without any sort of danger at all."

Aside from treatment by oil, the final avivage (during which the tile or clay red color that was there from the beginning slowly changes to clear red) is the most important operation of the process. Several researchers assert that it is first during avivage that the madder dyestuff in the fiber is joined with calcium and aluminum to gain the extraordinary light and color fastness (to laundering) that distinguishes the dyestuff from the actual Turkey red dye. At the same time the material is washed clean of the fat that is added during animalization.

The Limitations of Turkey Red Dyeing

The use of madder on vegetable fibers as described here was limited at first to dyeing cotton and flax yarn. In trade these yarns came in both lighter and darker tones and went under the name "Turkey rose yarn" or simply "Turkey yarn." Not until the beginning of the 1800s did it become possible to satisfactorily dye whole lengths of cloth a strong red color using a madder dyestuff.

It was not possible, however, to provide a cloth with a pattern and decor in Turkey red. The detailed and lengthy processes involved in getting the red color to attach itself to the fiber material precluded every attempt in this area. The red patterned sections that appear in older European cloth print (1700s and earlier) are the result of a special process, the "kettle dye print." These were applied with a thickened mordant on the cloth using stamps. When this was then treated in a madder bath, a red color formed on the treated areas of the cloth. But this did not have the Turkey red color's clarity and strength and its fastness was as a rule not as good. The formation of patterns in early printed fabric with relatively small red surface areas and an otherwise sparse coloring was more the result of technical than esthetic causes.

Ever since the seaway to India was opened and products from there began to pour into Europe, the dyers and printers admired and were amazed by the Indian multicolored cotton cloths. A professor at the science academy in Berlin and also royal Prussian Privy Council etc., Friedreich Hermbstedt, wrote the following in the *Magazin für Färber und Drucker* (Berlin 1811).

"The Indian calico (prints) were valued above all for their fastness and brightness, which when washed lost so little of their gloss that they instead became even more beautiful.

It seems an irony of fate that in the same year as this was to be read in the dyers' and printers' own professional publication, a page of the history of cloth print technology was being turned, and a new, revolutionary epoch was introduced. In it the Turkey red color came to play an all overshadowing role!

Turkey red cloth sample and formula. Page from test collection from Glarus.

"The Most Beautiful Cotton Cloths in the World Are Produced Here"

—Marco Polo, 1295

Indus – Indien– Indigo – India red

When several good factors interact, the result can be something singular, something unparalleled. In terms of technology, Slavic embroideries and the Anatolian textiles are made possible through abundant access to suitable types of fibers, dyestuffs, and mordant metals. Their esthetic form is achieved through a high level of human cultivation and the reflection of cultural currents in the products produced. The same favorable conditions existed at a similarly high level for the multicolored Indian cotton cloths.

While the western countries had been producing their dyed textiles using animal fibers for a long time, cotton was the dominant material in India for spun yarn. In the flowering cultures of the Indus Valley they had learned the arts of spinning, weaving, and dyeing cotton long before our chronology began. In the area where the most important discoveries relating to the Indus culture were made, the city of Mohenjo-Daro, fragments of madder dyed cotton fabric have been discovered together with various textile tools. The discoveries are dated to about 1,750 B.C.

India, named after the Indus River, has long been considered both the homeland of cotton and the cradle of textile arts. This is also the country where two of the most important and useable textile dyes of the world of color — blue indigo and red madder — were cultivated and developed.

Indigo was named after India in the 1200s and the madder dye was called India red as early as the 1600s.

Old print block, probably a company stamp from an Indian dye works and cloth printer (Laxmi dyeing).

Opposite page: Detail of an Indienne from Isfahan, Persia, dated to about 1750. Produced using a combination of resist, mordanting, and dyeing processes.

Some Literary Sources

The early existence and use of cotton in India is well documented in archeological discoveries. Despite comprehensive research, however, classical literature does not offer any deep insights into how it was produced. The oldest Indian sources to mention cotton are from the 800s B.C. and the Greek sources by the historian Herodotus are from four centuries later. It was not until the campaign of Alexander the Great in India, and the geographer Strabon's written descriptions of the rich colors of this multicolored cotton cloth, that the people of antiquity learned about the new textile product.

TE AMSTERDAM
By ISAAK TIRION, MDCCXXXI.

*Conversation about a map of India.
From a work by T.H. Salmon,
Amsterdam, 1731.*

*Opposite page: Calico print from
Isfahan, Persia. Dated to about 1750.
Used as a prayer rug. The Arabic
inscription contains a ritual prayer
formula.*

Of the travelers who crossed the known Asiatic parts of the world in the 1200s, Marco Polo left the best accounts of cotton and the various products made from it. He tells of the production of spices and dyestuffs as well as multicolored cotton cloths and thin gossamer veils in the various kingdoms that he visited on the Indian peninsula. We learn that products were shipped to Alexandria in Egypt from the kingdom of Malabar on the west coast, and that "the finest and most beautiful cotton cloths in the world were produced" there. Another, somewhat later, traveler wrote that in the presence of one such Indian patterned cloth he felt that "its flowers looked so natural, as if you were looking at a garden."

The Multicolored Cotton Cloths

In the presence of an Indian multicolored cloth, a person may be immediately struck by how skillfully drawn the flowers, leaves, and birds are, and by how well the numerous details of the pattern are arranged into interesting groupings. People who are familiar with the problems of dyeing technology are also filled with a great and deep respect for the skill of the early Indian dyers and printers. They had completely mastered the art of putting vat dyed-indigo, red madder, and other mordant colors on the difficult-to-dye cotton fibers.

It is also primarily knowledge of the mordant and resist processes that made the production of painted and printed cotton cloths possible, and this more than anything else gave Indian textile art its universal reputation.

China and Japan did not need the same knowledge of mordanting methods because the most important textile material in both countries was silk, which was dyed in the same manner as wool, using relatively uncomplicated mordant forms. The rhea fiber previously used in Japan was usually dyed with indigo in the same manner as cotton and other vegetable fibers.

A word long used in western European countries for the multicolored cotton cloths is calico (or calico print), from the Arabian *qoton*, which not surprisingly means cotton. We find a number of different names for the manner in which patterns were placed on these cloths — block print, resist print, mordant painting, resist dyeing, etc., — but the expressions are vague and do not give any good information about what the process actually involved. The often used term calico print is also very misleading because most of the dye is applied to the print by dipping the cloth and treating it in a proper dye bath.

Indian print stamp with a tree of life motif made with a copper border on a wooden base.

Opposite page: Indian calico print, probably from the first half of the 1800s. A combination of block print, drawing, and painting have been used in combination with resist, mordanting, and dyeing processes. The outlines of the larger shapes reveal the manner in which the kalam pen was used.

Processes for Producing Calico Prints

In brief we can say there were three different processes. *Mordanting* makes the textile material receptive to the dye in only the mordanted places, even if the entire piece of cloth is subjected to the dye bath. *Resist* makes the cloth reject mordanting and dyeing in the reserved locations. *Dyeing* involves treatment with the actual dyestuff.

Each and every one of these processes can be applied through block print, stencil print, painting on with a brush, or dipping. What is significant is that a component that is applied before dyeing stops the heat in a bath in which it is dipped.

The Mordanting Process

Mordanting can be done so that the entire cloth is prepared in a mordanting bath which contains alum, tanning material, etc. When the textile material is then dried, the desired pattern designs are applied by being painted on with a paintbrush, drawn on with a "kalam" pen (see page 124) or with a print block, a mordant dye (madder), or a metal salt (iron). The cloth turns madder red in the sections of the pattern where the madder dye is applied and black where the iron is applied. Both the dyestuff and the metal salt appear in a thickened form (dextrin, gum arabic, etc.). The entirely mordanted cloth can also be "piece dyed" in a madder red dye to be printed on by an engraving paste (enlevage print) later.

The mordanting substance can also be partially applied to the cloth on relatively limited surfaces with paintbrushes, pens, or print blocks. Depending on the form of application, it has a more or less thickening effect. When the mordant is well fixed and dried, the cloth is treated in a dye bath (madder). This permanently unites the sections that have been printed on with the dyestuff in the bath. After washing and rinsing, the areas where the alum and tanning material were applied become red, and if the mordant contained iron, they became black violet. As a rule the bottom becomes slightly tinted, but became whiter after repeated washing and bleaching.

A third form is mordanting and dyeing at the same time, which involves mixing a dyestuff with suitable mordant and thickener. The mixture can then be painted or printed on the untreated cloth. This method is commonly used to produce a green color. Yellow dyestuff plus mordant components are then painted on surfaces that were previously dyed with indigo.

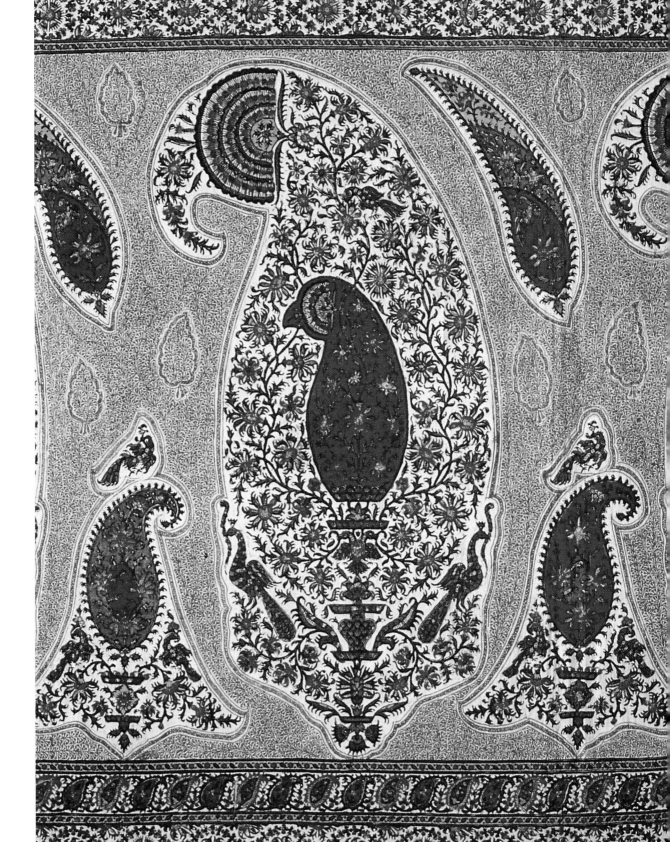

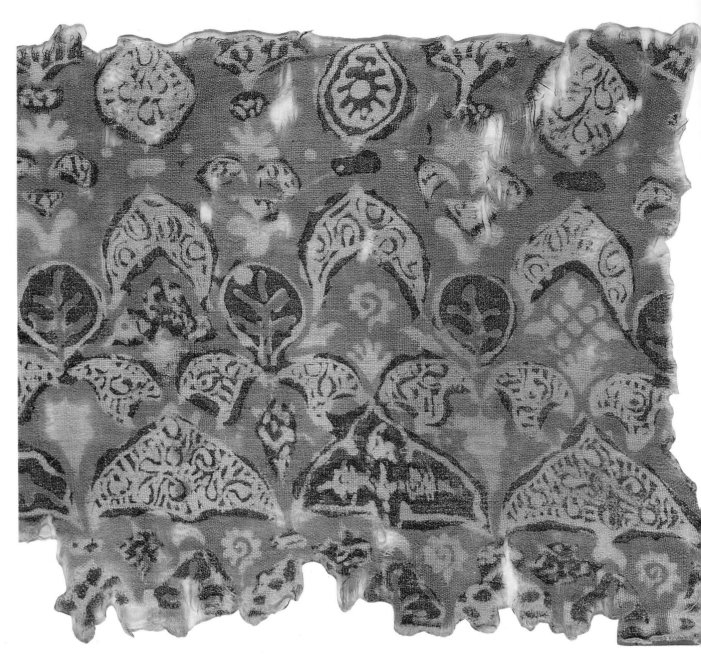

Textile fragment from Fustat, Egypt. The material is a thin, two-leaved twill cotton weave. The pattern is a result of a batik-like process using a kalam pen and a stamp. Two different dyeing methods appear to have been used, vat dyeing with indigo (woad) for the blue portions, and mordant dyeing with a madder bath for the red brown surfaces. The Fustat textiles are believed to have been produced in India or by Indian craftsmen living in Egypt. Similar textile finds have been made in various places along the coast of the Red Sea. The ornamentation in this fragment greatly deviates from what we are used to finding in these textiles, and this interesting circumstance makes it difficult to date. For various reasons the Fustat find has been dated to approximately the 1000-1500 period.

116

Resist Process

The resist process involves the use of a covering substance to prevent certain sections of the cloth from being dyed in a bath so that once the resist is removed, the undyed sections stand out against a dyed background. This process is commonly used to produce blue surfaces with indigo. Another use is to keep certain surfaces of an ornament red, while the remainder is intended to be turned violet through overdyeing with indigo.

The covering substance may be of very different types: pure beeswax, wax and resin, purified sheep tallow, rice, and other types of flour. In most cases the various materials are mixed together and the content and condition of the dye bath determines how they will be put together.

The resist can be applied with various tools, usually a wooden or a metal print stamp, press stencils of wood, or stencils of leather or rice paper, possibly even a single or multiple spout tjanting, plus paintbrushes of hair or plant fibers.

What Is the Secret?

Sometimes you find the statement that the success secret of the multicolored calicos was that the Indian dyers had access to an unusually large number of dye-producing plants and herbs, which is how the richness of the color and tint of the cloths can be explained. However, it is doubtful if this is where the true explanation lies. A capable dyer can always produce a large range of colors from a limited number of starting dyes by using different combinations of them and selecting different mordant substances and methods. Manipulation of these factors gives him a rich register of clarity and saturation — that is where the secret behind the art of dyeing lies, and that was what the Indian dyers mastered so early on and so completely!

But a calico print is also the result of a pattern creator's extraordinarily detailed, well-drawn master of the print blocks that were carved by hand with great feeling and the skill of a craftsman and the weavers' thin cotton cloths.

Korcula, the birthplace of Marco Polo on the Dalmatian coast

The home where Marco Polo was born in Korcula.

The Place Where Calicoes Were Produced

It is clear from Marco Polo's description that in those days calico print production had not only reached a high technical and artistic level, but also that production of them was widespread. He mentions production areas in both the northern and southern parts of the Indian peninsula. He informs us that the "great and magnificent kingdom Guzzaret" (now Gujarat in India) had indigo in great excess, equally as much cotton of which the finest muslins and other cloths were made, and that they made the "world's most beautiful and artistic embroideries" there. Gujarat is also where the often-mentioned Fustat Finds are believed to originate. The Fustat Finds are cotton calicos in blue and red with a characteristic white line ornamentation in unmistakable resist technique.

Another area that is known for its printed calicos is Bengal, that is the land area around the Ganges River and the lower part of the Brahmaputra River. This is where the British East India company opened its first trading stations in 1633, a farsighted event given that sales of these Indian multicolored cloths reached such a high level in Europe during the following century.

The Coromandel coast is probably the best known of all the production areas. In a work published in Amsterdam in 1731, author T.H. Salmon writes that the fastness of the colors is so high that they never leave the cloth, and he discusses the artistic form and beauty of the patterns. He also notes that the "Calicos that are produced on the Coromandel coast are decorated using paintbrushes while those produced in the north are printed with stamps."

Calico: A Piece of Floral Cloth

The travellers from various professions who visited India and who have been quoted in this book were all filled with wonder over the rich variety of floral calico patterns. It may seem strange that the patterns that awakened such enthusiasm for centuries are just as current and valued in today's textiles.

The basic patterns that occur in such abundance nearly all have flower motifs, either a single flower or a group of flowers, leaves, and stalks. One continually recurring motif in the Indian calicos and in central Asian art in general, is the *botha (mir-i-botha)*. There are few pattern designs that have allowed for so much skillful, artistic variation, although the calico pattern actually has a quite rigid form. The word *botha* is believed to be of Persian origin and means flowering bush, but has also been interpreted many other ways.

Even if both the dyestuff and the production methods are for the most part the same in the various regions, there is an incredibly rich variety of pattern forms. The various markets, both inside and outside of India, were supplied with very different, even "enriched" designs. Muslim areas have their special requirements and desires for picture content, as do Hindu areas, and the traders from western countries also had special desires for the format and pattern of the calicos.

The multitude of figures in the calicos included all sorts of birds, elephants, tigers and other animals, as well as buildings and figures in various situations. As gods and goddesses, they can dominate the picture; as flute players or soldiers they can march around the borders; or as couples in love they can wander around among animals and flowers in a paradise-like environment. All familiar and clear to those for whom the cloths were once created and at the same time exotically enticing and different for the new consumers in the western world.

When the Portuguese discovered the seaway to India and a number of East India companies were formed in the 1600s, the floral calicos streamed to the European trade houses in Paris, London, and Amsterdam. Cloths were valued for their fastness and chroma, their elegant, exotic patterns, and for the lightness of the material equally suited for articles of clothing and equipment purposes.

Production Sequence
for an Indian Calico

The methods used to produce Indian or Persian calico prints could vary significantly depending on access to mordants, dyestuffs, the skill of the craftsman, and artistic ambitions. The main steps in the production of an Indienne are illustrated here beginning with an old Indian print stock.

1. Production begins by applying the black outlines of the pattern. As a rule, a thickened iron fusion is used on cloth that has been impregnated with tanning material.

2. The second step involves application of a wax-resin resist on the surfaces that will later turn red and white. This is done with a paintbrush or a kalam pen.

3. When the resin stiffens, the cloth is treated in an indigo bath. After the blue dye oxidates, the resist is removed through vigorous boiling.

4. The red dye can be applied by different methods. The most common is to paint, draw, or print a madder dyestuff on the mordant-prepared cloth. Another method consists of applying a resist to the pattern surfaces that will turn white and blue, and then dyeing it in a cold madder dye bath. A process similar to the latter has been used in this example.

If additional colors are desired (usually yellow and brown) they are usually painted on with a paintbrush. As a rule they have bad fastness and bleach after a few washings. (See page 128.)

Is European Cloth Printing Really Cloth Printing?

To understand the enthusiasm for the Indian calicos we have to keep in mind what we ourselves could obtain in Europe at the same time. It is only in name, but not much more, that we can speak of the art of cloth printing in the Western world. In practice, methods for printing books and in the art of engraving were normally used. An oil-based pigment was applied to the surface of the cloth using crudely cut wooden print blocks. More than two colors were seldom used: black (often bone black) and red (vermillion or red lead). The binding agent was boiled linseed oil and the textile material was a coarse flax linen.

The result was a product where the color was mainly on the surface and allowed neither washing or wearing to any great extent. When the oil eventually hardened, the sections of the cloth that had patterns on it became stiffer, which meant that the cloth could not be used for clothing. The oily smell that accompanied this method and remained in the cloth was probably not particularly sought after.

These "cloth prints" had very little to do with the Oriental ones. In other words, the distance between Indian and European cloth prints was just as great as the distance between East and West, but contrary to Kipling's well-known words, they would meet anyway!

Print from Dalarna with oil-based pigment and stamp, probably from the 1600s.

Chronicling the Production of Calico Prints

It is natural that a product that was of such great interest on the European markets would be the subject of literary descriptions of the area where it originated and the methods by which it was produced. There are a number of descriptions from the 1600-1700 period of how the dyestuff was extracted and patterns were applied. They are written by visitors to India with various backgrounds — missionaries, scientists, and the agents of the French, British, and Dutch East India companies. Several of these works have been published, including several with fairly comprehensive commentary.

These descriptions are very valuable. They give us the background of the printing era that — inspired by the thousands of years old Indian calico print art — was further developed in France and Switzerland during the 1800s.

Despite efforts to be very accurate in these chronicles, both misunderstandings and exclusions have crept into the texts. Perhaps we shouldn't expect it to be otherwise. Even a missionary who was above reproach or a not-so-careful trade agent could not reasonably be expected to possess the knowledge of the elements of dyeing technology that are required in order to ask questions in a manner that would adequately bring out the facts about the most complicated of the dyeing arts. It is also doubtful whether the Indian dyers would really give their knowledge to a foreigner in more than a fragmentary state. In all times and in all cultures, dyeing processes have been guarded by the strictest rules of secrecy imaginable. In order to get a somewhat good picture of the processes, we need to reexamine the texts attempt to find out how the author might have misunderstood or incompletely described what he said. There should also be an attempt to make the picture complete through our own experimentation with certain production steps as well as allowing analysis of older Indian materials to strengthen or dispel doubtful hypotheses.

Despite the fact that the methods for producing Indian calicos mainly involved two color areas (blue and red) and a limited number of methods of application (mordant and resist), the combinations of these allowed surprisingly large number of different ways of proceeding. Some researchers and textile historians, above all the Swiss, have attempted to penetrate into parts of this complex field. They have also published interesting articles and works about it. However, it is outside the limits of this book to attempt to shed light on other and perhaps less well known parts. Instead, a description of the production methods written by the versatile French author, Jacques Savary, will be retold here with more or less detailed commentary. The description was written during the first part of the 1700s, published in an English edition in 1757 and in a German edition in 1811, with contributions by Hermbstedt in Berlin. Savary's description deserves to be studied because it contains the main steps found in several of the Indian and the nearby Persian pattern creation processes.

The interior of dye works, from Des Klugen und Rechts-verständigen Haus-Vatter's Buch, *1722.*

"Description of the art and the manner in which the Indian calicos, or Zize, are produced in India,"

—According to Jacques Savary

First Operation: Preparation of the Cloth

Before work on the calicos can begin, the cloth has to be bleached to half whiteness. A gall bath is prepared which contains the dried and pulverized shell of the cadu fruit and buffalo milk. The cloths are dipped and treated in this bath repeatedly, then they are squeezed out hard and allowed to dry in the sun. The following day they are washed and allowed to dry alternately in the sun and the shade. After this procedure, which is usually called "the inner preparation," a glazing takes place, the purpose of which is to make the surface of the cloth as smooth and even as possible before working with the pen and paintbrush. The cloth is folded into fourths or sixths and placed on a surface of Indian date tree, upon which it is beaten with a hard, round, wooden piece, *Catapouli,* until the desired evenness is reached.

Commentary

The cadu fruit comes from a medium-sized tree, which grows practically everywhere in the Indian woods. The most suitable type for production of calicos is obtained from areas along the coast of Malabar. The fruit is as large as a nutmeg and is used for its contracting effect and tanning material content, which greatly exceeds what European dyers get from gall nut, pomegranate rind, and sumac.

Second Operation: Application of the Black Contour Pattern

The cloth is now ready for application of the pattern design, which takes place with the help of a perforated paper model and pulverized charcoal from a small cloth bag. The procedure is similar to one formerly used by embroiderers. The contour lines that were applied in that manner are then traced in using a special pen, kalam, dipped in an iron-containing solution. As soon as the fusion makes contact with the tanning material in the cloth, the pattern contours appear in a black tone.

Commentary

The black contour design generally covers the entire surface of the cloth and serves as a basis for further steps and as boundary lines, primarily for blue and red pattern surfaces.

The iron fusion can be prepared in slightly different ways, but mainly by allowing heat-roasted iron cinders to stand in a vessel with acidic palm or coconut wine for a few weeks. The fusion should not contain too much iron, otherwise it may cause corrosive damage to the cloth and give it an undesired red tone.

The Indian pen, kalam, consists of a short bamboo stick with a metal pin at the tip and a "ball" of hair or plant fibers. The flow of the iron fusion along the metal pin is regulated by how hard you push it.

If a stamp is used to transfer the iron solution to the cloth, the solution must first be thickened to an appropriate consistency with the help of a flour or starch preparation.

Third Operation: Exclusion of the Tanning Material

After applying the black color to the intended areas, the cloth is treated in two baths, one right after the other. The first consists of nothing but rapidly boiling river water, while the second is supplemented with sheep or goat dung. In the second bath the cloth is treated overnight, then rinsed repeatedly and laid out in the sun. The Indian dyer says that this treatment is necessary so that he will be able to produce a blue color later.

Commentary

These procedures are important and absolutely correct. If the cloth in indigo dyeing still contains tanning material, the color turns black instead of blue. Another purpose of the treatment is to produce greater whiteness in cloth that previously was unsatisfactorily bleached.

Preparation of the Indigo Dyestuff

"You take the leaf of the *Avarei* or the indigo bush, which has been allowed to become very dry and you finely pulverize it. This material is transferred into a large vat filled with water, which is stirred now and then with a bamboo stick. The water is then allowed to drain through a hole that is toward the bottom, leaving the indigo behind on the bottom of the vessel. Remove the indigo and form cakes the size of pigeon eggs. Then strew ashes on a piece of cloth on which you allow the indigo to dry and then it is done. . ."

Applying the Indigo Color

"When the blue color is applied by dipping the cloth into a prepared indigo bath, rather than with a paintbrush, it must first be coated with wax. Only not in the places that are to be a blue or green color. The wax will be added there with an iron pen and just on one side. . ."

Commentary

Unlike mordant dyestuff, indigo dyestuff is insoluble in water and therefore cannot directly dye a textile fiber. It must first be converted to a soluble form with the help of a reducing agent in an alkaline bath. After the textile material is treated in the dye bath, the indigo dyestuff is formed again through an inverse process (oxidation) to its insoluble form. It is then anchored stably in the fiber from which it can only be removed using extreme measures.

The dyeing process begins by treating the cloth in rice water, drying it and beating it in the same manner as described earlier. Then a resist wax mixture is applied to the sections of the pattern that have to be protected against the blue dye (the surfaces that will later remain white or be dyed red). By laying the cloth in the sun for a while, the wax goes through to the other side. The resist consists of beeswax and a smaller quantity of resin which is applied with a kalam ("iron pen"). The cloth is then turned over to the blue dyer, who eventually returns it dyed.

Fourth Operation: Preparation for and Red Dyeing

"After the blue color the red will be added, but the wax must first be removed from the calico, bleached, and prepared so that it can absorb the red dye."

Commentary

This preparation takes place by boiling the cloth vigorously several times, treating it in sheep and cow dung, and treatment in an emulsion containing the tanning material (which contains the cadu fruit), as described in the beginning. Through this process the cloth is well prepared for the requisite impregnation in fatty buffalo milk, which precedes the dyeing itself. The procedure, which has a decisive impact on the final results, must be done with the greatest of care. The milk is worked into the cloth with your hands.

When all the different preparations are ready the cloth will be sent to the red dyer, who often lives in a very different place. For success, a dyer must have access to a well with "hard" water (calcium containing), which is not so common, even in India. A city or region often had no more than one single well of this type.

Chaya (Chay root) Dye

"According to some, Chaya or Essaye is a variation of a "dye madra." The root is pale yellow and a beautiful red dye is prepared from it which is then used to dye cotton cloths from Mesulipa, making them very esteemed."

Commentary

The modern understanding is that "dye madra" is a type of Galium (Galium triandrum). The red dye can be extracted from several different Indian madder plants, but the roots of a plant called Chadar or Chaya (Oldenlandia umbellata) are often used. They are used dried and could previously be purchased in bundles at the market places in India.

Before the roots can be added to the dye bath they need to be finely pulverized in a stone mortar (a wooden mortar was considered unsuitable), while "hard" water was carefully added. Depending on the type of nuance desired, greater or lesser amounts of alum are also added.

Applying the Dye to the Cloth

Savary's introductory description of the preparatory measures in Chaya dyeing well matches the Turkish red dyeing processes used in more recent times. Later on in the text about the application of the dye on the cloth, however, a misunderstanding seems to have arisen.

After having described the preparation of the Chaya solution the text continues: ". . . finally add the calico was dipped into this dye. . . and when the hand can no longer stand the heat of the dye bath, then the person who wants to make the product beautiful and perfect does not fail to take it out of the bath and dry it. . ." Then there is a long description of how to remove the color flakes that appeared when the dye was painted on the cloth, and the text continues: " . . . when the flakes have been removed the calico is put back into the bath. . .toward evening, the fire under the vessel is increased and allowed to boil for one hour. Then the fire is put out; when the dye bath cools you remove the cloth, squeeze it out, and allow it to lay until the next day. . ."

Where is the author's misinterpretation of the process? As one of the preparations for the red dyeing it is indicated that certain sections need to be protected by the application of a coat of wax. But the sequence indicates that an increasingly warm, even boiling, bath is used, which would totally destroy this layer of wax, as well as destroy its purpose of protecting the surfaces that are supposed to stay white and blue respectively (in a later stage even yellow and green) after dyeing.

A warm bath is usually only used when a completely unpatterned product, or when a partially applied, thickened mordant emulsion is being dyed on an untreated cloth.

A logical and technically reasonable continuation of this "operation" would be to partially apply a thickened dye by painting and printing it on the mordanted cloth. Following drying and avivage aftertreatment, the red sections of the pattern and the exteriors should be kept along with the blue and white ones. That this next step should be the right one is supported by the text's description of the color flecks that can appear when the red color is painted on! If you study the older calicos, you are even more convinced of this interpretation. That a misunderstanding of the type related here occurs can be explained because none of the chroniclers of the calico process were able to obtain a collective picture of the calico print production process because the various stages were completed by specialized craftsmen who lived in completely different locations.

Fifth Operation: A Violet Red Color

This short section describes how mixing the red Chaya solution with a certain quantity of black iron fusion (see page 124) and rice wine that is as sour as vinegar produces a solution that makes a violet red color. By adding the ingredients to the solution in various proportions, a range of colors can be produced, from weak grey violet to dark brown violet.

Sixth Operation: Various Red Colors

"You can make several colors that correspond to the red Chaya dye, which we do not find necessary to discuss here."

Commentary

This short passage in Savary's account does more than just inform us that it is possible to produce red colors other than the Chaya root color just described. It indicates a condition, the effects of which often perplex those who study the Indian calicos. The red dyes are certainly related, but contrary to what many believe, a uniform procedure can not used in the dyeing processes. The Chaya root can be dyed in warm baths just like ordinary madder, while several Morinda types can be dyed in cold baths. Different resist and pattering methods must be used when dyeing and printing using these dyestuffs.

Seventh and Eighth Operations: The Yellow Color

"What remains is to talk about the yellow color, which doesn't require any detailed explanation. The same color that turns green when you paint it on blue also turns a yellow color when you paint it on the white calico. Only this color is not particularly durable."

Commentary

Sometimes certain sections of a calico pattern are applied using a yellow mordant color, which is preferable when you want to make the leaf ornament a green tone. This was accomplished by painting on yellow dye thickened with starch gum. Ingredients included flowers from the cadu bush, pomegranate rind, and alum. Unfortunately the dye, as Savary points out, had low fastness and could be strongly bleached after just four or five washings. Subsequent treatment with certain plant substances, usually well-preserved secrets, could increase the fastness but at the expense of the brilliance of the color.

"Persia is a Large and Vast Country"

—Marco Polo, 1295

Detail of the border from an Indian calico print. The crackled exteriors show a wax-resin resist that is used for the indigo blue color.

Kalamkari: Persian Calico Print

Ever since the Shah Abbas the Great (1588-1629) left his residence for Isfahan, multicolored, hand-printed calicos were produced there along with other skillfully produced textiles. We know them by the Persian name kalamkari, or *Qalam-kar,* which in translation means pen *(kalam)* and work *(kar).* The same word also appears in India, while in Persia the Sanskrit word *Cit (Chitta)* is used, meanings speckled or multicolored cloth. The western term for a multicolored cotton cloth of high quality — chintz — comes from that word.

India and Persia are considered the main areas for the use of mordant-patterned textiles. The selection of motif, dyestuff, and the production methods have long been (for the most part) the same for dyers from both areas. The Persian dyers used a different work process to apply the dye to the cloth than the one found in Savary's description. Textile researchers are a little uncertain of the methods used for applying the blue color.

The Indienne above is from Isfahan, Persia, dated to about 1750. A detail of the same is to the right. Produced through a combination of resist, mordanting, and dyeing processes in combination with block print, painting, and drawing (with the kalam pen). Dyestuff analysis showed that the red dyes contained "pure alizarin" (from madder dyestuff), which indicates that some form of Turkey red dyeing was used.

The Technique for Producing Kalamkari

When we speak of kalamkari production we often distinguish between an older and a newer form. The former used exclusively natural materials and involved a greater number of processes. The latter also used a number of artificially produced dyes and assistants, but the procedures were simpler.

In brief, the work process involves the following main steps.

1. The desizing, washing, and bleaching of the textile material.

2. The gall and oil treatments of the cloth with Myrobalan, gall nut, pomegranate rind, and fatty buffalo milk; drying.

3. A paste that contains green vitriol, castor oil, gum dragon, and water is printed on the areas of the pattern that are to turn black.

4. Another paste that consists of alum, gum dragon, red clay, and water is applied to the areas that are to turn red.

5. The cloth that has been handled in this manner is then treated in a madder bath. The iron mordant printed on the surfaces appears black, and areas treated with the alum mordant become red. The background becomes a weak, cream-colored tone.

Commentary

The processes are unlike the Indienne, where the iron fusion, which gives the black color, is applied through a completely separate introductory process.

Myrobalan is a strong tanning material containing fruit from *Myrobalanus chebula*, which grows in India, on Sri Lanka, and on the islands of the East Indies. The red clay earth serves as a "mix dye," making it possible for the dyer to see if the impression of the stamp was clear and properly placed on the cloth.

130

The Application of Blue Indigo

Indian calico print with botha *paisley motif; first half of the 1800s.*

Older accounts of Persian cloth printing have been written by European travellers, and modern researchers have contributed to them with attempts to explain the kalamkari technique, but as yet there are no complete interpretations. The most obvious example of this is when we attempt to explain how the blue indigo dye was applied to cloth. The Indian wax resist method, which resembles the batik process, is not considered to have been used in connection with kalamkari print. Alfred Bühler commented on this in one of his works. "The accounts I know of regarding the production of kalamkari mention mordant dyeing with madder dyestuff, but not the accompanying batik resist for indigo blue. This dye is printed on the cloth in a soluble form, and is not oxidized until it is applied to the cloth. From this it can be assumed that at least the newer calicos produced in Persia with wax crackling are not made in that country, but have been imported from India."

Commentary

The most suitable and perhaps the most common method for applying indigo on textile fiber is through treatment in a regular dye bath. But for knowledgeable indigo dyers it is entirely possible to paint or print the blue color on a cloth with the help of a thickened stamp vat which is equipped with a suitable oxidation and drying retardant substance (some type of urea, for example). Studies of older textiles from areas outside of Persia reveal that the method of affixing a reduced indigo solution, which is then allowed to spontaneously oxidize on the material, is not entirely uncommon.

131

The Blue Red Family Treasure

Ajrak - Pakistani calico print

Calico print, ajrak, from the province of Sind in Pakistan.

For centuries a form of calico print that is noticeably different from both Indian and Persian prints was produced in the province of Sind in the Indus Valley. Its name, arjak, is believed to be an old Arabic word for blue and indicates that the process may date back to a time when the province's cloth print was produced using a simple clay and resin resist and was only white and indigo blue. More recent ajrak had, and to a small extent still has, a powerful color range of blue black, madder red, and white. As a rule, the design is strictly geometric with a centrally placed field surrounded by small framing edges or small patterned bands plus a couple of broad ending borders.

The production method resembles Indian or Persian in many ways, except that no kalam, or "iron pen" as Savary calls it, is used. Resist and mordant pastes are applied before respective dyeing using wood stamps of various sizes and designs.

Even if the contours of a calico pattern were applied through the introductory process using pulverized charcoal (page 124), the use of the kalam pen with flowing wax or an iron solution allows relative freedom to create personalized individual lines and details. It may seem at first that the use of print blocks would give the pattern a more mechanical and poorer appearance. But by varying the direction of the print block, the distance between sections of the design, and arranging different blocks in new constellations, the skilled ajrak artist can produce designs with great vitality and movement. The best quality, and therefore the most expensive, are printed on both sides, requiring great skill.

The ajrak cloths were previously used for many different purposes and they were worn by nearly everyone in society — men and women, rich and poor. People wrapped up in them when they slept or set a festive meal on them. The white harvest of the cotton field could be collected in them or they could be used as prayer mats when the crier read from the mosque tower. Bridal couples' arjak turbans were carefully preserved for generations as valuable family treasures.

Opposite page: Calico print, ajrak from the province of Sind in Pakistan. Two different stages of production, the lower one is after an iron fusion was printed on.

The Canton capital Glarus.
Watercolor by J.H. Jenny, 1834

East Meets West

Thoughts of a Calico Print Manufacturer

"The introduction of the Indian calicos to the markets of the western countries is a milestone in the history of cloth print, and modern cloth print production is intimately related to the textile art of the Orient. Spinning and weaving of cotton fibers was done in prehistoric India, as documented in the oldest Sanskrit literature. The art of printing ornaments and figures of different colors on cotton cloth also dates back to an indefinite and remote time. Strikingly, the saturated blue, red, brown, and yellow colors in these prints without exception are both durable and chemically fixed to the fiber, allowing the cloth to keep its material sensitivity and character."

This is what the Swiss calico print manufacturer Adolf Jenny Trumpy related in the introduction of an account of the production of calico prints, which he hosted for the historical society in Glarus at the end of the pervious century. For more than two centuries these multi-colored cotton cloths played a dominant role in textile production in Europe, and as far as we can tell, this will be the case for a long time to follow.

Calico Fever

In an earlier section we read about how travellers and professionals expressed their unconcealed admiration for the Indian calicos they saw when travelling, or in the small shipments that were brought into Europe. When transport by the ships of the British, Dutch, and French East India companies really got underway during the 1600s and 1700s, it became possible for an even broader public to enjoy these renowned cotton cloths. The reception was as dramatic as it was enthusiastic, and had consequences that none could have predicted.

The new products were imported under many different names, depending on where they came from and in which language they were described. The first common names were Indiennes or Persians, indicating their countries of origin, India and Persia. They were called *Toiles peintes* and *Toiles imprimés* (painted and printed cloths) in France, *Pintados* ("painted" cloths) in Portuguese, and printed calicoes and *Kattun-druck* in English and German respectively.

The popularity of the Indiennes and the rate at which they were imported increased at the same pace. Soon the finely woven cloths with their artistically printed and painted patterns became the day's topic of conversation in large social groups. Some have even described it as the outbreak of a "calico fever." No description, however, can more accurately illustrate this phenomenon than that by the Englishman Daniel Defoe (the author of Robinson Crusoe) from 1708. With poorly hidden irony he wrote the following:

"These people's obsession with products from India has now reached the painted calicos, which were formerly used for quilted blankets and clothing for lower class children. Today they are even used by our finer women. The power of fashion is so great that we have seen persons of rank wearing Indian cloths even though only the maids were allowed to use them before. The queen herself has been seen in Chinese silk and calico. But this is not enough. These cloths creep into our houses, apartments, and bedrooms. Curtains, pillows, cushions, and finally the bed clothing itself; yes, practically everything that was formerly made of wool and silk, both for women's clothing or our homes, now comes from Indian trade."

The increased sale of Indiennes in France created an unexpected situation. The East India Company could not bring in enough quantities of the sought-after product. The reasons were the small-scale form of production and the strict production methods by craftsmen. Some skilled craftsmen — at that time France was a leading country for production of finer textile weaves — decided to attempt to produce calicos in a manner similar to the Indian and Persian dyers and printers.

Production of Indiennes in Europe

The religious consequences of the repeal of the Edict of Nantes in 1685 excluded the Huguenots from most occupations, but they saw an opportunity to provide for themselves by what appeared to be an extremely doubtful way of making a living. Their new product — Indiennes — was a big success, and eventually the producers of silk, velvet, and wool products began to suffer increasingly noticeable economic losses. The Huguenots had the monopoly in this industry, and the government eventually considered it necessary to enforce a special ordinance forbidding all production and sale of these "painted cloths." Violators were subject to very severe punishment. An unavoidable, and for the French economy unfortunate consequence of the ordinance, was that the Huguenot printers who earned a good living from their production of calicos emigrated and transplanted their knowledge to other countries. Some fled to England, where calico production was not yet prohibited. Others fled to western Switzerland were they founded businesses that were to become the greatest producers of Indiennes. Their *Toiles peintes Neuchâteloises* (painted cloths from Neuchâtel) were exported to far and distant markets. The great manufacturers even had their own warehouses in France, Italy, and Germany. At international fairs in Basel, Frankfurt, Genoa, etc. they both sold their Indiennes wares and studied fashion trends in cloth print.

The European Indiennes competed successfully with the Indian and Persian original prints for the favor of consumers on the continually expanding markets. The intense interest in floral cotton cloths can be seen in a letter from the philosopher Jean-Jacques Rousseau, dated 1764, where he writes: "If we are going to survive, we must soon begin to eat clocks and Indiennes, because farming is completely neglected of the sake of these lucrative arts. . ." Rousseau's interest in cloth prints once came close to a bad ending. When he was a little boy, he was playing in his uncle's (the Huguenot descendant Fazy's) factory and attempted to start the great calendering machine. Fortunately, particularly for those of us who later would share his thoughts and his musical works, the incident ended with only a couple of chopped off fingertips.

Opposite page: One of the most famous workshops for producing printed calicos during the 1700s in France was in Jouy, near Versailles. It was started and directed by the German-born Ch. Ph. Oberkampf. The most valued of the prints from Jouy is probably Les Travaux de la Manufacture from 1783, which shows the various production phases at a calico print workshop. In the foreground the artist Huet is seen working on a pattern, with Oberkampf and his little son diagonally behind him. The top half of the pattern includes a hanging or drying tower, preparation of cloths, and various forms of printing with blocks or engraved copper plates.

The Franciscan's Fight Against Prohibition Paragraphs

The strict French calico print ordinances intended to protect the domestic wool, velvet, and silk trades were later bitterly regretted by the rulers. For long periods the French women would play endless annoying tricks on the authorities in their fight for a coveted product. But they did not fight alone. In the shadow of the regulations, a well-organized smuggling business flourished. Large quantities of calicos made their way into the country in the baggage of diplomats and through other routes from Holland, Germany, and Switzerland and on small fishing boats via the English channel from England. Neither the galleys or the death penalty that hung over the heads of the smugglers had deterring effects. The forbidden floral cotton cloths reached their nice customers via thousands of channels. With their many actions and clever tricks, these consumers maintained a veritable "fashion war" for nearly seventy-five years. Authorities in Paris could even confiscate the calico clothing of women caught wearing it in the open street, and one account describes the burning of no less than 800 calico evening gowns.

The Wave of Prohibition Spreads

Conditions in several countries were similar to those in France. In 1700, William III of England instituted a law against the importation and use of Indian printed cloths. In 1727 the law was rewritten to cover all calicos, whether they were produced in England or anywhere else. On paper these laws were strict, but the British hardly obeyed them. In Germany, where strong and detailed ordinances regulated the import of foreign calicos, people were heavily fined and the products were confiscated and publicly burned.

The kalam pen can be used for applying both wax resist, dye solution, and iron fusion.

Detail of a printed calico, Indienne. It is clear that red sections of the reproduced pattern were applied with a kalam pen. Note that the artist forgot or purposely omitted a smaller portion of the botha form's border lines. Only the gods are capable of completing things!

The Dilemma of the European Indian Printers

The hand-printed Oriental calicos and their European counterparts are produced under relatively similar conditions and techniques. The European printers also had the ambition — and the public the desire — to imitate the floral language form as closely as possible. The result was that for a long time there was an obvious similarity in patterns between the Indian and the European calico prints.

The bottom material for the Indiennes was cotton cloth, and the limited assortment of mordant and dyes of the day caused extraordinary difficulties for both dyers and printers. It was necessary to produce a product that possessed satisfactory use fastness and came in a variety of clear tones. Because of the realities faced by calico printers, technical matters (instead of the intentions of the pattern creators) determined the appearance of the European prints. The veins and flower stalks on the pattern were drawn as thin black lines and the dyed areas, including the red ones, never covered any large surfaces. The gracious multitude of forms on the print were usually outlined against a white or weakly toned background, creating a light, airy impression. A trend toward large-scale production and the introduction of various mechanical devices during the second half of the 1700s did not noticeably change the appearance of the Indiennes.

Opposite page: French calico print, possibly from Jouy, dated to around 1780. Dyestuff analysis showed that the red sections of the pattern were dyed with madder.

Sampler embroidered with Turkish red cotton yarn, dated 1874.

The Turkey Red Calico Prints

A Time of Change

Toward the end of the 1700s and during the first half of the 1800s, a series of important events occurred and revolutionary innovations were made in cloth printing technology. Nearly every decade brought significant news that would influence the entire field of dyeing technology and the esthetic form of the calico prints to the extreme.

The most decisive event occurred in 1747 with the disclosure of the long-kept secret method for dyeing madder on cotton materials (Turkey red dyeing). In the description it was emphasized that the method was only applicable for dyeing yarn and entire lengths of cloth, an annoying circumstance that chemists and dyers attempted to find a solution for at any price. In connection with the dyeing of indigo on cotton material a method called blue printing had been used for centuries in which a resist was applied to the areas where a pattern picture was desired. After dyeing, the pattern was white against a deep blue background. But the use of a similar process in connection with Turkey red dyeing was out of the question. No paste could withstand the many aggressive processes that brought the red color to the cotton cloth. Instead, entirely different methods had to be used.

Recipe from a handwritten recipe book, 1776.

Monogram embroidered with Turkish red cotton yarn, second half of the 1800s.

A Revolutionary Idea

During the first decade of the 1800s in France there was eager experimentation to discover a new mordanting process for the wax dyestuffs used in cloth printing. In connection with these attempts, an unproven method was used — the application of etching paste — to remove one dye while having that same etching paste deposit a new dye in the place where the pattern was etched off. This new method made it possible to remove one dye while applying the new one in its place *at one and the same time*. An advantage of this process was that you avoided having annoying missing sections between the various sections of the pattern, and the process was soon raised to a form that was equally complete and revolutionary.

The Red-Bottomed Merinos

In the city of Mülhausen (now Mulhouse) in Alsace, a production business of finer cotton weaves and Indiennes was founded in 1746. The three promoters — J. Schmaltzer, H. Dollfuss, and Samuel Koechlin — are mentioned in the literature as unusually skilled manufacturers and idea-filled innovators in their fields. The same is true to a particularly high degree of the descendants of Samuel Koechlin, who in a decisive manner contributed to bringing cloth production into a entirely new technical and esthetic era.

Around 1809, the manufacturer Nicholas Koechlin & Frères produced an article that quickly became a great success. It went under the name of red- bottomed Merino and was a Turkey red dyed cotton cloth with a black decor (iron and tanning material) of a richly formed *mir-i-botha* motif. This print made Turkey red a part of calico print production in Europe.

Daniel Koechlin's Discovery

In 1811 the company's multi-talented colorist, Daniel Koechlin, noticed that the Turkey red dye, which normally showed a noticeable resistance to alkaline chloride of lime (bleaching lime), was immediately destroyed by chloride of lime when combined with an acid. Because direct printing on this etching medium was unfeasible for several reasons, Koechlin figured out another way. Using a stamp, he printed a thickened acid (vinegar) on the red colored cloths, then he treated them in an alkaline chloride of lime solution ("the decoloring vat") for a few minutes to destroy the red dyestuff on the printed sections. The result was a white pattern against a Turkey red base.

Soon afterwards he discovered that the mineral dye "Parisier" blue (also called "Berliner" blue and other names) resisted free chlorine, so if this dyestuff was added to the etching paste, the printed sections became a lively blue. After applying the blue he used a paintbrush or print block to add a yellow mordant dye (berries from alder buckthorn (*Frangula alnus*) on the white sections to get yellow and on the blue sections to get green. In that way he achieved an entire range of dye tones.

White etching. Sample print from Blumer & Jenny.

Opposite page, top: Turkey red calico print with the botha motif from Mulhouse, 1830s.

Opposite page, bottom: Calico print samples, multicolored Merinos from Mulhouse, dated 1824.

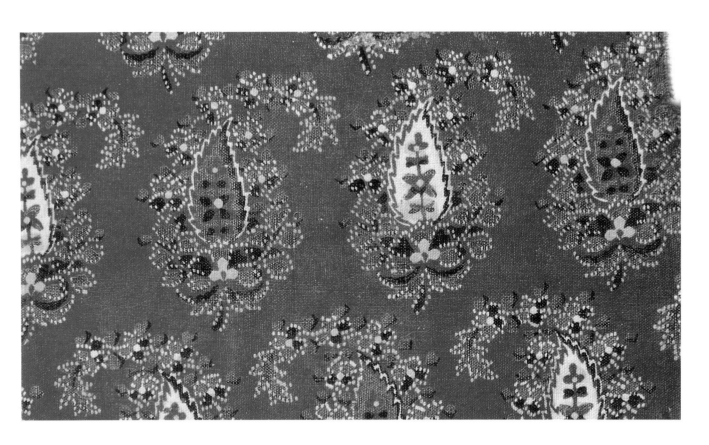

1824.

de mm. Thierry-Mieg.

a. Mulhouse

145

The Multicolored Turkey Red Calico Prints

Daniel Coechlin's continued experimentation led him in 1820 to the discovery that chrome yellow (lead chromate) could be used to etch madder dyed cloths. The method was named yellow etching, and resulted in a special product that was, for the most part, intended for scarves and shawls called simple Merinos or Yellow-red Merinos. A brief description of the production methods follows.

Add a soluble lead acetate (sugar of lead) to a thickened white etching paste (with tartaric acid) which can then be deposited in the fiber in the same place where the red dye is destroyed (and the fiber becomes white). When the cloth was dipped in a solution of chrome acidified potash (potassium dichromate), lead chromate (chrome yellow) was precipitated in these spots, creating a yellow pattern against the red bottom color. This method gave a dye that was superior in both light and washing fastness and which soon replaced the formerly used yellow colored mordant dyestuff. This dye also became an important coloristic influence on the so-called multicolored Turkey red calico prints on the continent, most commonly known as Illuminating Merinos.

The name Merinos, used as early as 1809 to describe the first black red prints, was inspired by the then very popular European version of the famous cashmere scarves. These were woven from the wool of the Merino sheep, the whiteness of which gave more brilliant dyeings than other types of wool. Koechlin not only took the name Merino, but also the ancient Persian-Indian *botha*-motif that made up the main pattern of the weave. He allowed the skillful designer, L-J. Malaine, who moved from Paris to Mulhouse, to create endless variations of this pattern for his Turkey red calicos. From the beginning it was naturally enough called the cashmere motif, but later it became more and more common to use the somewhat misleading name of "palmette" pattern, called paisley today.

A Circle Is Closed

The Eastern red cloth prints are produced using an extremely lengthy and labor intensive process. For several centuries their European counterparts were produced using techniques that were almost as difficult to master. Through the ingenious efforts of Daniel Koechlin and a handful of other cloth printers, the East Asian dyers initiated a way to print madder red on cotton material.

The blue indigo color had dominated folk textiles in Europe for centuries. No country, no city was without a workshop in which "blueing" the beloved "blue print" with white rose stems and a deep blue bottom were produced. With the red Merino cloths it now became the strong red madder dye, that together with a number of Oriental patterns, became the most desired folk color. East and west would thus not only meet in multicolored Turkey red calicos, but also be intimately woven together.

The Production of Calico Prints in Switzerland

It wasn't only in western Switzerland that Indian workshops were founded primarily by Huguenot refugees or manufacturers who were descendants of Huguenots. Cloth printers also worked successfully in other cantons and in Zurich.

The production of Indiennes was in may ways pure craftsmanship with the individual printer's treatment of the heavy stamps a decisive aspect of the product's quality. The task of the printer was by no means easy. For example, there are cloths in which hundreds of different blocks were used to produce the final pattern. There were also the so-called pencilling girls, who painted in all the additional areas by hand.

Print stock for calico prints with a peacock motif owned by Blumer & Jenny, Schwanden.

Sample print from print stock above.

Handkerchiefs from the turn of the century.

After the introduction of the roller printing machines, the entire printing process was simplified and several countries began to assert themselves in the field of cloth printing, causing serious trouble for many people in the calico print industry. In order to protect this new industrial branch, high protective tariffs were instituted to impede export to the markets that the Swiss companies had built up. The largest and most famous of the printers in Geneva and Neuchâtel were forced to close their businesses in the 1820s, and only a few Indiennes producers survived the tough competition. The calico printers in the Canton of Glarus fell into this category, they experienced a heyday during the 1800s. An industrial economic report from 1865 indicates that no less than twenty-two textile printing houses with over 6,000 employees produced over 48,000 km of cloth every year — enough to surround the globe. In no other canton did textile printing reach such an extent as in Glarnerland during the second half of the 1800s.

The calico print industry in Glarus was at such an exceptionally high level from the 1820s that experts and printers emigrated and started similar businesses in other countries. We know that Michael Weber from Glarus built the first roller printing machine near St. Petersburg as early as 1814. A few years later, with a number of capable professionals and capital, both from Switzerland, he started a factory for dyeing and printing at Zarewa, near Moscow.

"Glarus, the Economic Wonder"

It may seem strange that they managed to create an industry of such an extent and significance in Glarnerland, in such a small surface area and under such unfavorable circumstances. Perhaps the author W. Senn touched on one significant reason when, in 1770, he described his impression of the people of Glarner in the following manner: "Nobody is as hard-working and enterprising, nobody knows so well how everything can be used. . . at each of the world's trading centers we will probably meet somebody from Glarus."

One reason for what has been called the "Economic wonder in Glarus" is that several of their businesses established trading connections in foreign markets and set up trading houses all over the world. At least equally important, however, was that they aimed to produce "appropriate designs" using a definite format that could not satisfactorily be reproduced on the new Rouleaux print machines. The efficient new techniques that were developed in Mulhouse were carefully guarded and the Turkey red "handkerchiefs" and calicos became synonymous with Glarus and Switzerland all over the world.

In 1740 the Landmajor H. Streiff and the colorist Fazy from Geneva started the first cloth print works in Glarus. A factory for piece dyeing with Turkey red and Indian production was started in the canton's capital in 1779 by Ch. Trümpy. It would become one of the most significant in the country. Another well-known Glarner business, P. Blumer & Jenny in Schwanden, will be described in more detail below. But it should be pointed out that many others were operated just as capably and with the same happy results.

Few textile products have ben so universally spread, and been found on the markets for as long of a time, or been used for as many different purposes, as these Swiss "Schnupftücher" (handkerchiefs). They were used in the sense of the original meaning of the word as handkerchiefs by Norrland's railroad construction crews, by mountain climbers, and by provincial doctors in the city. Of course they have been an obvious part of the clothing of ox drivers on the Pampas and cowboys on the prairie, and have also been worn as a beloved neck scarf or head covering by Turkish or Macedonian weavers in Galicnic and Maras.

"We Will Start a Red Dye Works with God's Help"

January 7, 1828

The Trading House of P. Blumer & Jenny

Pattern master from Welker & Hubner, Paris, for multicolored Marino prints. Blumer & Jenny, Schwanden.

The Blumer business was founded in the beginning of the 1700s by councilman Peter Blumer from Nidfurn near the district of Schwanden in the Canton of Glarus. In the beginning, they traded yarn, cloth, and produce, but after taking partners from his brother-in-law's family, Jenny expanded the business by adding cotton cloths and calico prints. In 1788, when he was seventeen years old, one of the grandchildren of the founders, Peter, established a branch office in the Italian harbor town of Ancona. Living insight into the various large and small problems experienced by the company can be found in the correspondence between Schwanden and Ancona. For example, problems included the purchase of a "crimping machine" for the wool fringes that trimmed the head cloths or *Türken-kappen*, intended for Turkey, and the recruiting of printers and colorists.

Many businesses that did etching (single or multicolored Merinos) did not always produce the Turkey red bottom material themselves, but left this time-consuming production to specialized dye works. However, a letter dated January 7, 1828 states that "We will start a red dye works and hope that in doing so, just as with everything else, to achieve success with God's help."

One thing that you notice in this connection is that the order books during these years always started with "In God's name, amen" and ended with "amen." It is surprising how often a strong religious overshadowing has helped them take risks on one hand, and to endure misfortune on the other. In May of 1830 Ancona reported that "everything is going friction free and we are now working with seventy-eight printing tables, but the old factory must be rebuilt if we want to increase production even more." In October of that same year they had one hundred tables, which meant that about three hundred people were employed in the printing of calicos.

A Global Business

The economic and political situation in Europe at this time was extremely unstable, a troublesome situation for all businesses. Reducing the consequences of trade conditions on the market and of the protectionist measures required the support of as many reliable export markets as possible. The Blumer operation had the advantage that it had established connections early on with markets outside of Europe.

Some examples from the order books also confirm this. In April of 1831, a shipment of shawls was sent to Rio de Janeiro, and the following year a shipment went to Calcutta, and so on. Contact with the Balkans and the Far East led to the establishment of a trade house in Bucharest and joint ownership of another in Smyrna. From 1847 they even had a sales office in Manila, where they had a consular appointment for several years.

The trade house in Ancona was responsible for the sale of Blumer products to south and central Italy, Spain, Portugal, the Balkans, and Turkey. Exports went via Vienna and Trieste to Russia and the Middle East, as well as via Hamburg to South and North America and to Scandinavia.

In addition to the Ancona office, they owned a piece of land in Italy that was as big as the entire canton of Glarus, upon which they bred silk worms and farmed. They also operated a shipping company and owned a fleet of five large clipper ships that transported products all over the world. Pope Pius IX travelled to Ancona in 1858 to participate in the christening of the ship Helvetia, a testimony to the reputation enjoyed by the company.

Pattern master for multicolored Merino prints. Blumer & Jenny, Schwanden.

Product labels for markets outside of Europe. Blumer & Jenny, Schwanden.

Hanging tower from 1850 at the Blumer & Jenny company, Schwanden, in the canton of Glarus.

The Hanging Tower:
A Different Type of Building Construction

For obvious reasons, cloth print works, dye works, and bleachers were located near a river or lake at the edge of a community. In the beginning, a print works required a great deal of craftsmanship and only a handful of employees to operate, so one building often sufficed for all production. But the larger and medium-sized businesses that eventually developed from these, required more buildings because each step of the production process required its own, and often very special room. Space was needed for the many printing tables, for pattern designers and form stitchers, for handling dyeing and washing. As the century progressed, an "oilery" where the cloths were impregnated with an oil emulsion for madder dyeing was also needed. Because the risk for self-ignition from the oil in textile material was so great, and from time to time caused devastating fires, the buildings were often located a safe distance from each other.

Special buildings for drying longer pieces of cloth, with individual hanging arrangements, already existed during the early period of calico printing. One such building is pictured in the well-known print from Oberkampf's workshop in Jouy near Versailles. Newer constructions, that were better suited for the increasingly complicated produc-

Building for drying longer pieces of cloth, from Oberkampf's print, 1783.

tion processes, resulted in a completely new and very different type of building, the so-called hanging tower.

The buildings of a calico print works formed an organically coherent and architecturally interesting picture in the community. The Blumer print works included about eighteen buildings for various purposes, of which three were hanging towers.

The air hanging tower (*Lufthänge*) consisted of a stone walled base or a ground extending up into a predominantly wooden construction with several floors. As a rule it was clapboard supplemented with tall Venetian blinds for use in controlling air flow in the drying room. Under the ceiling projection there was a walkway for hanging lengths of cloth to dry, especially on days with a hot and dry chinook wind.

It was in the 1800s that the hot hanging towers (*Heiss-türme* or *Heiss-hänge*) began to be used, and heated air was used to dry cloths that were being dyed Turkey red. The actual tower was completely walled in stone in a square area with few windows. Lattice work bars on the roof were used to hang full lengths of cloths.

Between 1830 and 1880 in Glarnerland, they began using buildings that were a combination of manufacturing and air hanging towers. These buildings had a walled portion a few floors high where the print rooms and other rooms were set up. Above this section were air hanging towers constructed in a manner similar to the one just described. Because every calico print works needed one or more hanging towers, these buildings were long a characteristic feature of the landscape of Glarus. Of these special industrial markers only a few, including two belonging to Blumers in Schwanden, remain today.

The Hohlenstein business in Ennenda, Glarus. Drawing by Toni Strolz.

Pioneers in the Social Area

Blumer & Jenny were not just skilled in their own area of business. Their business was characterized by an unusual social consciousness for those times, which attracted attention and led to enduring pioneer efforts in the social area. Thus they belonged, inspired by the example of Rochdale, to the pioneers of consumer cooperation when Schwanden opened its first consumer owned store in 1869.

By 1853, a business social foundation for workers and service men had been started — which served as a modern pension insurance — and it still exists today.

The first worker protection laws in Switzerland were established in 1864 in the canton of Glarus. The first factory inspector, Dr. Schuler, who himself was a resident of Glarus, managed, despite a great deal of opposition, to drive through legislation. In agreement with manufacturers and workers he carried out valuable social reforms and provisions.

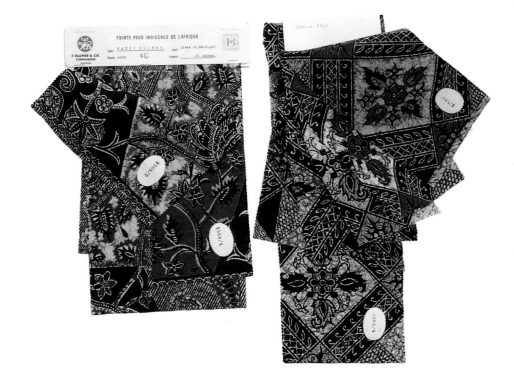

Batik print for African markets.
Blumer & Jenny, Schwanden.

"This is a Country
of Exceptional Beauty"

Conrad Blumer's Trip to Java, 1840

A unique wealth of motifs and articles was produced by the Blumer business during the 1800s. The individual colorists were responsible for the majority of the designs, but to a certain extent originals were purchased from some of the great pattern studios in France.

One of the greatest sales successes for nearly a century, primarily for Blumers but later also for other Glarus printers, can be attributed to the outcome of a trip that one of the company's employees took to India and the Dutch East Indies (now Indonesia). His name was Conrad Blumer, and he eventually compiled his diary notes into a 260-page volume, which is now preserved at the company in Schwanden.

Diary quotes and information have been obtained from that document, which may answer questions that textile historians and researchers of costume have long asked. Among their questions is why, in certain areas of Africa, costumes and hip garments have been worn on festive occasions that were decorated with purely Javanese batik ornaments. Or, what is the background for finding calico prints with the same floral patterns and color scales in Macedonian, Albanian, or Turkish mountain towns, as in the areas around Siljan in Dalarna (Sweden). In clothing collections of many Russian folk art museums

Conrad Blumer (1817-1882), partial
owner of the Blumer & Jenny
Company, Schwanden.

154

from Moscow down to Baku in Azerbaijan you can find nearly identical Turkey red prints, although it's noteworthy that even on these prints there are a number of decorative elements that belong in the East Asiatic island world's resist techniques such as ikat, plangi (tie dye batik), and wax batik.

On April 8, 1840, Conrad Blumer started his long trip — which would not be without hardships and drama — from Marseille, via Alexandria, Suez, Bombay, and Calcutta to Batavia (now Jakarta) in Indonesia. His "travel journal" (in the form of letters home to the company) differs noticeably from those of other travellers quoted earlier. It contains nearly nothing about the land and people he meets. On the other hand, in the introduction you meet a man who fits author Senn's description of the able businessman from Glarus whom you could meet everywhere. Serious and duty-bound, Blumer was a man who in his letters had little left over for other than that which was the purpose of his trip. He describes his own task with the words: ". . .to acquaint myself with what is in demand in various locations, the sale of which, on the other hand, is the responsibility of the agents, and that is what he gets paid for." Using few but expressive words to describe his situation, he says: "I want to be able to feel the pulse of the market."

Some additional quotes have been selected from his letters to Schwanden. In one of them we discover the thoughts of the industrialist Blumer regarding the situation of other marketers and textile manufacturers. In another quote, the Glarus resident shows restraint in describing his own hardships and privations during the trip. The later quotes give a pictue of a partially new Conrad Blumer, attributed to his meeting with Javanese batik art. You experience his changed selection of vocabulary and enthusiasm for this textile product, as if he were someone who found Pandora's box. The future would also prove that the hope it contained would become reality — yes and even more!

During his trip to Madras, Conrad Blumer was amazed about the progress and standards of the domestic textile industry. ". . .Despite the inferior methods and very imperfect tools, spinning, dyeing, and printing are done extraordinarily well here, yes so skillfully that not only silk, but also cotton cloths are exported to Europe in great quantities."

The next stage of the journey to Calcutta, for which Blumer harbored such great expectations, nearly ended in tragedy. The ship was stranded and sank very close to its destination, but Blumer saved his life and — what he probably considered equally important — his cloth samples. However, the cloth samples suffered a great deal of water damage. In his laconic style he writes the following about this: "I have had an unpleasant trip on my crossing with Hoogly, and can not thank the heavens enough for saving my life, which a large number of people on the ship were not successful in doing. . ."

A Javanese nobleman dressed in a batik patterned festive costume. Observe the acute angled motif on the leg. From Raffle's History of Java, *1817.*

Letter from Conrad Blumer to the company in Schwanden in which he describes Javanese batik production.

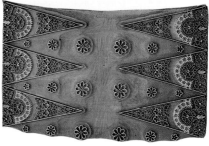

Print stamps with ornamentation derived from Javanese batik. Blumer & Jenny, Schwanden.

Opposite page, top: Batik from Semerang, Java, with acute angled motif (Tumpal), around the mid-1800s.

Opposite page, bottom: Test sample for batik print made around 1843 according to a prototype from the Javanese original works that Conrad Blumer brought home from his trip.

Across the Bay of Bengal to Java

The next stage of the journey was Java, "renowned for its seven kingdoms, the island of gold and silver," as the Indian national poet Ramayana called it. But this sea journey was not particularly pleasant for the already tried Blumer either. The journey that was supposed to last between twenty and thirty days lasted nearly two months and "was accompanied by all sorts of horrors because of a shortage of fresh water. . ."

One day, when the Javanese volcano mountain stood outlined against the mother of pearl haze, Blumer could agree with Linné's student, Thunberg, who had been plagued by an equally difficult trip: "Finally we caught sight of the island of Java, and were not just a little bit happy to arrive at a country, that was the goal of the desires of so many. . ."

The commissioner in Batavia showed him "great friendship," and perhaps it was together with him and during the trips that they took together that he experienced ". . . a country of exceptional beauty." Several other sections of the letter may have made a greater impression on those at home in Schwanden who were awaiting the results of his trip. "There is really a great need for dyed cotton products in Java," and "Batavia will make a great place for our products. A great deal can be delivered there at good prices."

"Together We Will Attempt an Imitation"

Conrad Blumer's experience of the beauty of the Javanese landscape and the treasury of patterns in its batik art make up the most emotionally charged and colorful lines of his diary. In a letter dated February 10, 1841, he describes batik production and the various garments decorated with it. "This is the famous batik genre, but nobody has as yet succeeded in producing the same genuineness in the colors or in imitating patterns in an equally good manner," and "I will bring this style of sarongs to you and together we will attempt an imitation."

In the middle of August, 1841, Conrad Blumer returned to Schwanden, his trip a success. He made contacts and analyzed the needs of various markets for Blumer's products. One of the most important things he did was to bring back patterns and textile samples that served as suggestions and ideas for new products.

The job of transferring the batik samples he brought from Java to cloth prints began immediately, and his intention of imitating the original as exactly as possible succeeded beyond all expectations. The Blumer & Jenny company thereby produced an important new calico print product, the batik print.

157

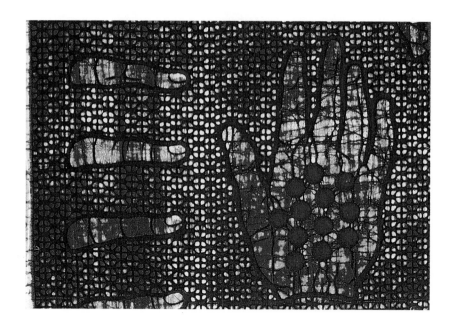

Javanese Batik – Glarner Batik – African Batik

The Peculiar Path of a Pattern

When batik prints were made there was an effort to imitate not only patterns, colors, and cloth qualities, but also to adjust them to the shapes of various Javanese clothing, specifically the slendang (shawl), the sarong (tubular cloth), the head cloth, etc. The carefully made Glarner imitations controlled the Javanese markets for decades, along-side domestic production.

The first batik prints intended for use as sarongs (1842) were produced by Turkey red etching, and were exported not only to Indonesia but also in large quantities to India. The following year the Blumer company even succeeded in imitating the classic high Javanese blue-white-brown batik works. This was accomplished using a white resist and dyeing in an indigo vat. The soga brown color was painted in by hand with a catechu (cutch) dye that turned out to have good fastness.

Later the company produced sarongs and slendangs using mordant dyes and madder. In all of these processes, the dyes had to be applied to both sides of the cloth to ensure the sought-after batik look. This made it necessary to use a very complicated engraving process using two matching print stamps for each section of the pattern, a process requiring great precision from the printer.

Blumer & Jenny remained the sole producers of batik prints for a decade, but then one company after another began similar production. In the latter half of the 1800s, the Gebrüder Greuter & Rieter trade house in Islikon in the canton of Thurgau became well known producers of indigo blue and Turkish red batik products. Until World War I, the Swiss calico printers kept their leading position in the production of calico prints in the Dutch Indies and the Philippines. The colonial powers themselves then became suppliers of batik imitations, and after World War II domestic wax batik production regained much of its former importance.

From time to time attempts were made to produce this product in a manner that required less time and labor. Toward the end of the 1800s experiments were done where a heated resist paste (wax and resin) was applied before the cloth was treated in the indigo vat.

The Hohlenstein company in Ennenda-Glarus improved and could finally expand this process by machine. In brief, the method consisted of applying the heated wax resist on the textile material with tanned copper rollers. The surfaces with the print on them soon stiffened and were made to

Calico print, yellow red Merino, with a motif of acute angles, from Blumer & Jenny, Schwanden.

crackle, the cloths were put into the deep indigo tanks. When sufficient nuance depth was achieved and the resist was removed using a series of strong washings, the color-intense direct dyes were printed on with wooden stamps. This so-called Swiss batik was in very high demand in west Africa from Senegal to Zaire right up until the company closed in 1972. It was considered one of the most popular textile materials for festive clothing.

Many producers of batik prints used the technique of promoting the crackling effect as their starting point and considered it the criteria for "genuine" batik. Regardless of what other efforts were made with respect to the pattern formation on these prints, the crackling effect remained the most sought after and indispensable attribute. New markets and new names for products did not change this factor.

In the Blumer company's production during the second half of the 1800s, you find another tangible result of Conrad Blumer's trip. Inspired by the many textile samples he brought home, the company's colorists began applying completely new and different floral patterns to the Turkey red Merino prints. They now added the Javanese acute angle (*Tumpal*), the peacock (*Burung merak*), the dragon (*Naga*), and many other motifs to

Multicolored Merino print from Blumer & Jenny. Calico is decorated with both Indian, Persian, and Javanese pattern elements.

their formerly predominantly Persian and Indian motifs, primarily the *botha* motif. The overall distribution of the fields also followed the Javanese designs from sarongs and kainpandjang (articles of clothing) by having rhombuses or square center fields dominate the pattern which ended in borders on the other edges with small patterns.

There is strong evidence in these prints of a melting together of the Javanese batik's rich floral patterns and the early European illuminating calicos. Perhaps that was also exactly what Conrad Blumer really intended with the many samples he brought home from his trip. In the prints from Blumer & Jenny we meet the new pattern forms without an excess of the annoying crackling effects.

Perhaps these multicolored Turkey red colored calicos, seen in a greater perspective, will find their place beside the ancient blue prints. We can now experience the madder red and the indigo blue prints as the Ying and Yang of the art of cloth printing. Opposing powers that work together in an esthetic constellation.

Woman in a wedding dress from the Prelip area of southern Macedonia.

Scarf, Ouskolets, *of multicolored Turkey red calico print. The scarf is part of a wedding dress from the Prelip area of southern Macedonia. From a drawing by Marija Malanova, Skopje, 1963.*

Sample print on an Ouskolets *scarf from Blumer & Jenny, Schwanden, mid–1800s. During the 1800s this print was exported to Turkey, Macedonia, and Scandinavia, among other places; from Blumer & Jenny.*

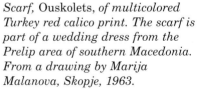

"Genuine" calico with the peacock motif. From Insjön, Dalarna.

163

Kaftan, Khalat, from Samarkand. This old court and civil service officer's costume from Turkistan of ikat patterned silk cloth is fully lined with multicolored calico prints. One of the two botha motifs that dominate the exterior of the pattern is green, which indicates that the calico may have been produced for Muslim customers. (Green is believed to be the color of the coat of the prophet Mohammed.)

Turkey Red Calico Prints in the Costume Customs of Dalarna

Luxury Ordinances, Smuggling, and the Peddlers from Västergötland

Following the trend in the continent, authorities in Sweden attempted to put the breaks on the economic and moral damage caused by the importation of cotton calicos. This was done by implementing so-called luxury ordinances, that were intended ". . .to restrict or do away with the use of certain cloths and clothing fashions, products and stimulants that are considered damaging to the economy, health, and morals of the people. . ."

In the same manner that the calicos reached their customers in Europe in an endless stream, they also spread among us, to high and low, to city and country people. The main intermediaries of the red cloth prints were the peddlers from Västergötland, the wandering house-to-house peddlers. Their path to their recipients was as difficult and full of danger as their assortment of goods was valued out in the countryside. This was less a result of the length of the roads or the changing climactic conditions and more because many of the sought after goods were smuggled in, and as such were subject to the inquisitive interest of customs officers, county officials, and other fiscal people.

Opposite page: Sofia in a "kråka" (a bonnet) from Gagnef, Dalarna. The outer cloth is of ikat patterned cotton weave from the first half of the 1880s. It is lined with multicolored Turkey red calico prints from the latter half of the 1800s.

Girl's bonnet of Turkey red calico print, so called multicolored Merino. Dalarna's Museum, Falun.

In the great work *Ett år i Sverige* (1827), it is said that the peddlers were only allowed to sell products that were made by the Swedish country people " . . . but they also bought and sold many others, mainly products that had been smuggled in. . ." That was probably the case, and in 1795 the Swedish Board of Commerce reported that significant confiscation of smuggled goods occurred as a result of searches of the products offered for sale by the house-to-house peddlers from Västergötland.

There must have been significant quantities of illegally imported products that were sold in the country during the time of the luxury ordinances, but for obvious reasons there are a number of difficulties in penetrating into this bit of Swedish economic history. It has also logically been designated "our unknown economy."

Scarf, Turkey red calico print, so-called multicolored Merino, from Dalarna's Museum, Falun.

KIND.

"Knalle," house-to-house peddlar, from Kinds (rural) district. Drawing by J.G. Sandberg, from Ett år i Sverige, 1827.

Tritik patterned breast cloth (= kemben) from eastern Java.

How the Calico Prints Got to Dalarna

The peddlers were not themselves "printers" of Swedish products or importers of smuggled products from abroad. For obvious reasons they were supplied mainly in Göteborg with both legal and less legal products for their journeys into the countryside. Many of the country's largest trading houses and wholesale dealer companies were in Göteborg, and that is also where the East India Company, formed in 1731, was located.

In the 1917 issue of *Fataburen* we can read the following in the annual chairman's report of the Nordic museum. ". . .Dalarna constantly stands out as the treasure mine of our peasant culture, still powerful and fertile. . . for example preserved articles of women's clothing include a great number of dresses, under-bodices, and aprons in various stripes characteristic of the parish, as well as a number of articles of clothing of so-called Falun cloth. These were usually made of printed calicos in distinctive patterns that had limited distribution within the province. They were purchased from Vienna by the wholesale dealer H. Münich in Falun exclusively for sale in Dalarna and that is how they contributed to the special character of Dalarna costumes. . ."

"Hårkulla" (Dalecarlian woman who travelled around selling things made of hair) from Våmbus at a stand for producing lace for hair products. Her scarf is a so-called "Russian rag," a calico print in red and yellow.

Scarf, yellow red Merino. Through the trips of the so-called "hårkulla" to and from Russia a large number of calicos were brought home to Dalarna that looked like this one. As in this example from Dalarna's museum in Falun, many of them have the triktik centered mid-field.

The appearance of red calicos in this part of the country has given rise to many questions and speculations. Despite how few words they contain, the annual reports may make it possible for us to answer some of them. The first one is that the source of the rich abundance of red calicos, precisely in the Dalarna area, could be attributed to the wholesale dealer Münich. It is interesting that the text goes on to say that he limited his sales to this part of the country alone. This factor, combined with the illegal sale of calicos to the people of the Siljan district by the peddlers from Västergötland, contributes to the character of the Dalarna costumes. It is also interesting that the annual reports mention the exotic and apparently foreign design element in the decorations on "Falun cloths." They are considered "unique," which nobody can blame the author of the texts for saying. Little did he realize what the true source was for the patterns created by the colorists at the calico manufacturers.

That wholesaler Münich purchased his calicos from Vienna did not necessarily mean that they were produced there.

Scarf, "yellow collar" from Insjön, Dalarna. Calico print from the early 1800s.

This calico print scarf from Dalarna's Museum shows us the first forms used to apply patterns to a Turkey red dyed bottom. It was probably made by applying an iron preparation (for the black surfaces) and an etching acid (for the white sections).

By the 1800s, printers in Glarus either had a trading house or agents in several different locations in Europe. According to preserved journals, significant quantities of printed calicos were supplied to Austria-Hungary among other places.

In addition to the sale of printed products by peddlers from Västergötland and Münich's sale of printed products to the people in Dalarna, the number of yellow red Merinos brought home via the trips of the "hårkullar" to and from and Russia was considerable. These scarves were called "Russian rags," and were common in Mora and Våmhus by the turn of the century. These yellow red scarves are still used in Våmhus costumes.

We have answered a few questions regarding the red calicos in the Dalarna folk costume, primarily their origins and how they were produced. Unfortunately, our knowledge about the way that the textiles got to Dalarna is uncertain and remains for the most part unknown. There is room for interesting and urgent research efforts on this topic.

Opposite page: Johanna in a costume from Rättvik with a scarf of multicolored calico.

Detail of pattern knitted sweater, Roses, by Lena Nordström. The various red tones are dyed with cochineal alone or with a mixture of madder and cochineal on wool yarn that was treated with alum mordant. A couple of the dyes were subsequently treated with iron (-sulfate).

MODERN FORMULAS AND INSTRUCTIONS

For Dyeing with Madder, Cochineal, and Mushrooms on Wool Material

There are various reasons why people still want to dye their own yarn or cloth. The first one may be the need to produce a red textile material for a certain purpose. Another motive can be the possibility of experiencing the exciting, visually dramatic moment when unpretentious material is turned, through dyeing, into a shining red color right before our eyes. Another goal can be the value of experimentation, which, as was pointed out earlier, enriches our understanding and brings the dyeing process and its mechanisms to life.

The formulas have been well tested over a long period of time so that someone without any training in dyeing should be successful in achieving results.

The selection of recommended mushrooms used in this book is motivated by their technical and coloristic relationship to both madder and cochineal.

The Technique of Cochineal Dyeing

Introduction

Natural dyes are usually divided according to the method used to get the dyestuff to fix itself to the textile fiber during the dyeing. We have talked about two separate types of dyestuff: vat dyestuff and mordant dyestuff. The indigo and purple described earlier belong to the former type, while the dye scale insects, including the cochineal, belong to the latter.

A mordant substance consists of various metal salts that create an affinity between the textile fiber and the dyestuff. We often use mordant formation as a type of glue between the dyestuff and the fiber. The mordant can be added during various stages of the dyeing process. Perhaps the most common method is to prepare the fiber with the appropriate metal salt *before* dyeing. In other cases the mordant can be added to the dye bath itself and is allowed to work together with the dyestuff. In still other cases the mordant is added toward the end of dyeing, or even as a special treatment after dyeing.

Many mordant metals have the ability to change the dyestuff's color in a characteristic manner. So by selecting the mordant metal you can produce a lasting bond between the dye and the fiber, as well as strengthen the visual qualities of the dye's color tone, clarity, etc.

Of natural dyestuffs, cochineal is the one that produces the most beautiful colors and the best chroma. This is especially true when yarn is mordanted with tin salt (tin solution; see page 55) and dyed in an acidic bath. The word scarlet, which in the beginning generally referred to a cochineal color, eventually became associated with the brilliant strong red color that can be produced with the help of tin. With significantly less chroma, a deeper and bluer color called carmine can be obtained using alum mordant. Weaker dyeings produce rose tones that are clearer than those obtained with madder. Chrome pre-mordanting produces violet colors that can become very dark and deep.

Practical Advice for Dyeing with Cochineal

The most advantageous way of dyeing with cochineal is in an acidic bath. This is particularly important in chrome mordanting, where the color is not absorbed at all if the bath is neutral or alkaline.

The cochineal color is unbelievably sensitive, even to very small quantities of metal combinations (usually iron and copper) in water or from the dyeing vessel. The color becomes less brilliant and approaches violet (in worse cases the color is destroyed), and the fabric becomes gray without a trace of color.

Because the dyestuff is intensely colored and easily dissolved, cochineal is well suited for nuances, especially yellow colors. It can be added at any time during the dyeing process, although the process should continue (for the sake of fastness) at least one half hour after the final addition. In this manner very intensely colored orange dyes can be produced if tin mordanting is used and if a yellow dye is selected and strongly beautified by tin, for example quercitron, apple tree bark, or birch leaves. As a surface color or in overdyeing on indigo, cochineal on alum mordant gives a clearer violet and blue-violet colors than madder does.

Cochineal dyeings have good fastness on all mordants, five or better if the dyes are at full strength.

Scarlet Red on Wool
Cochineal and Tin Salt
(according to Sandberg & Sisefsky, 1982)

Ingredients	a.	b.	c.
Yarn (wool)	100 g	100 g	100 g
Cochineal	5 g	8 g	15 g
Tin salt (stannus chloride)	1.5 g	2 g	3.5 g
Wine stone	5 g	10 g	15 g
Hydrochloric acid	3 ml	4 ml	8 ml
Water (soft)	5 l	5 l	5 l

The yarn for this recipe must be unmordanted!

Preparations

Cochineal is weighed and finely ground in a porcelain mortar (not metal!), and should be softened the day before dyeing if possible. Cochineal is added to the water, the temperature of which is kept at the boiling point for 10-15 minutes. The dye bath is skimmed off and the brown black precipitation around the inside of the vat is wiped clean. Then all the chemicals are added and the bath is allowed to cool off to below 90°C.

Dyeing

The yarn is moistened in warm water (at a temperature that you can put your hand in), squeezed out, and treated in a dye bath about 60 minutes at 90°C. It should be drawn on rods the first 10 minutes. Note that the dye is absorbed very quickly!

The yarn is washed and rinsed, the final time with water made acidic with vinegar. Dry.

Commentary

The recipe is a modern version of the recipe from 1762 (see page 55). It gives intense red colors in three different saturation ratios. The color is alkaline sensitive so the color change can occur during treatment in fulling liquids, for example.

Crimson Red on Wool

Cochineal on alum mordant
(according to Sandberg & Sisefsky, 1982)

Ingredients	a.	b.	c.
Yarn (wool)	100 g	100 g	100 g
Cochineal	3 g	10 g	25 g
Alum	20 g	20 g	20 g
Wine stone	10 g	10 g	10 g
Water (soft)	5 l	5 l	5 l

Mordanting

The yarn is mordanted in alum for 60-90 minutes at 90°C. It is an advantage for it to remain in the bath until it cools or until the following day.

Preparations

Cochineal is weighed and finely ground in porcelain mortars. It may be softened the day before dyeing. Add water, the temperature of which is kept at the boiling point for 10-15 minutes. The bath is skimmed and the brown black precipitation around the inside of the vessel is wiped clean. Wine stone is added and the bath is allowed to cool to below 90°C.

Dyeing

The alum mordanted yarn is moistened in warm water (at a temperature you can put your hand in), squeezed out and treated in the dye bath for 60 minutes at 90°C. Draw on rods the first 10 minutes. Wash the yarn, rinse, and dry

Aftertreatment

An afterbath can be used on alum-mordanted yarn (20:100) as long as useable dye remains. To get maximum use of the bath, vinegar is added to make the taste very sour.

Commentary

This recipe is a modern version of the Carmison recipe from 1762 (see page 54) and gives a violet red color in three various saturation ratios. The color is well-suited for overdyeing with indigo.

The Technique for Dyeing with Madder

Madder on Wool and Other Animal Fibers

The distinction has been made in this book between the use of madder for dyeing wool and animal fibers on one hand, and for cotton and vegetable fibers on the other. The division was motivated by the great differences in assistants and techniques that have to be applied to both dyeing and printing on various types of fibers. Many modern handbooks on dyeing with plant chemicals ("dye drugs") did not make this distinction as clearly as would be desirable. Thus you can read in otherwise beautiful and attractive books that "the dyeing process for linen and cotton is the same as for wool." But it is recommended that a stronger dyebath be made than the one in the recipe for wool. Such statements are misleading and will result in some dyers being disappointed. If we study some of the many handbooks that were published during the 1700s, though, we find that they always gave different recipes for dyeing madder with wool than madder with cotton.

Like cochineal, madder belongs to the so-called mordant dyes, and the mordanting stage itself is the part of the dyeing process and is responsible for the durability and color appearance of the red dye. Many of the mordant bath's metal salts also have the ability to change the color of the dye in a characteristic manner. Thus we can, through our selection of mordant metal, control the madder red dye within a very wide range, both with respect to color tone, lightness, clarity, etc.

Mordanting with Alum

Alum (potassium aluminum sulfate) is the most common mordant metal for dyeing madder on wool material. Unlike other mordants, it does not notably change the actual color of the mordant dye. Normally 20 g of alum is used per 100 g of textile material (when dyeing with plant dyes), but in strongly saturated madder dyeings it is advantageous to increase this to 30g/100g material. Any further increase has certain disadvantages because it makes the wool material sticky and can cause the fiber to become brittle. Usually mordanting is done in a separate stage before dyeing (pre-mordanting). Sometimes the dyeing process is simplified by adding the alum to the dye bath itself (mordanting at the same time). In madder dyeing, however, this procedure is less common because in certain ways it decreases the durability of the dye.

Thoughts about the Degree of Acidity of the Mordant Bath

The most common textile assistant in alum mordanting is wine stone (cremor tartari), which is used in the dyebath in varying quantities. There are hardly any instructions in the art of dyeing that do not recommend its use, yet there are no technical documents explaining why it is necessary or what happens to a dye if the textile material is without it or gets too much of this additive. Although several researchers noticed the relationship long ago, their observations seem to have been completely ignored by everyone who has published handbooks on the subject in this century. A few short excerpts from several works from the 1700s will throw light on the situation.

"The amounts of alum and wine stone, and the proportions between them, vary greatly between the various dye workshops. If you increase the quantity of wine stone to a certain point, then you get a dark cinnamon dye instead of a red dye, which however is durable. As we have seen, acids give the madder dye a yellow tone. Hellot has calculated 5 ounces of alum and 1 ounce of wine stone for every pound of wool yarn, while Pörner recommends even less wine stone, namely only a seventh of the weight of the alum." The above text comes from a handbook for dyers by the French chemist Claude Louis Berthollet, published in a German translation in 1792. Similar thoughts were advanced in a Swedish-Danish dye book from 1768/72.

"Depending on whether you want color and shading on the cloth, you use these preparatory materials (alum and wine stone) in different proportions; even gall nut and alkaline or lye salts can be used."

Jan Sisefsky, a chemist and physicist familiar with dyeing, has critically reviewed and explained the background for the thoughts of the old dye chemists. Through his investigations and experimental work, we now have the opportunity to improve our understanding of the steps used in the initial mordanting stage of madder dyeing. This information allows us to consciously control our chances of reaching our goals with respect to color.

Chemically, wine stone works by keeping metal salts in solution under conditions where they could easily precipitate. If the wine stone were not added, the salts would form insoluble combinations, falling to the bottom of the liquid and no longer reacting with the fibers. The use of wine stone is therefore a manner of ensuring that the entire quantity of mordant material used really fixes itself to the fiber, so that you don't get a weaker mordant than you anticipated, and, consequently, a weaker dyeing.

When we use wine stone in the mordant bath we must be aware of two important factors. The wine stone is a weak acid and if it is transferred to the dye bath via the mordanted yarn it can in many cases counteract the absorption of the dye. Like other acids, wine stone can also influence the color tone of the dye so that the madder gives yellower tones. Since alum pre-mordanted yarn is often allowed to dry without rinsing, it is necessary to think about rinsing the yarn well before dyeing. (Soaking the yarn before treatment in a dye bath, for example.)

It is also possible to neutralize acid with ammonium hydrate or potash (ash lye), controlling it with pH-paper. The old dyers, who in many cases knew the negative effects of wine stone, had to satisfy themselves by judging the color and taste of the bath, and test dyeing it until they saw that the bath was in the proper condition.

Color Changing Mordants

Some metal salts and assistants not only have the ability to bond a dye to the fiber, but they can also more or less strongly change the original color at the same time. Various types of iron products have been used since time immemorial for this purpose. Water containing iron and sludge containing iron and clay have been used in this manner in Japan to produce a deep black indigo tone on resist-patterned textiles, and in western Africa as a direct dye on the so-called Bokolanfini weaves from Mali. In old Swedish recipes you find the expression "slip-gör," that is iron ground into fine particles and mixed with water. Analysis has shown that the brown violet color on coptic woven fragments has, as in the photo examples in this book, turned out to be madder mordanted with iron.

Iron has a powerful effect (called "saddening") on dyes, making them both darker and blacker. Today, iron is used in the form of green vitriol (ferric sulfate), often together with some tanning material, tannin, or gall nut.

Iron is worth using to produce color, but it's somewhat doubtful in terms of practicality. Large quantities of iron can damage the fiber. Ten grams of green vitriol to 100 grams of yarn is the maximum that should be used. Dyeing black using tanning material and large quantities of iron is not be recommended. Old rya rugs, and sometimes Oriental weaves, often contain black dyes with up to 50 percent iron per fiber weight, which causes the dark portions of yarn to break down so that the weave looks relief cropped. Black colors are best produced by a suitable mixture of dyestuff, for example deep indigo with a saturated madder dye, possibly with the help of moderate amounts of iron.

In order to beautify the fiber, the green vitriol is added toward the end of a dyeing, and the yarn is not treated longer than about fifteen minutes once the iron is added. For the same reason, the yarn should not remain in the bath to cool off.

Another metal that has been used in dyeing for centuries is copper. Copper was one of the first metals that people learned to recognize and extract, and they also found methods of getting the metal into a soluble form early on. Today only soluble copper salts are used, of which blue vitriol (copper sulfate) is the cheapest and most common. Blue vitriol is mainly used for its darkening effect and is always combined with more effective mordant, usually alum.

Copper darkens the color in a completely different manner than iron. The color becomes deeper, but tends to keep its pigmentary qualities. In madder dyeing, it gives a warm, red-brown color.

As a rule, copper is added to the dyebath, when yarn needs to be pre-mordanted with alum. The addition can take place in the beginning of the dyeing since the copper is absorbed and darkens very slowly. Copper can also be added at the end of the dyeing and it can be discontinued once the desired color change occurs. Sometimes blue vitriol can be added during pre-mordanting with alum. Copper normally does not damage the fiber material, but the largest amount added is 20 grams per 100 grams of yarn.

Dyers did not begin using chromium on a large scale until nearly the end of the plant dyeing epoch in the 1870s. Chromium darkens the color and draws it toward violet. The light fastness increases significantly, as is usually the case with chrome-mordanted dyes. Chrome-mordanted dyes are also used in wool dyeing with synthetic dyestuffs (chromium complex dyes).

Tin has a certain beautifying effect, but not as dramatic as with the dyestuffs of the cochineal group. It is mainly used in Turkey red dyeing.

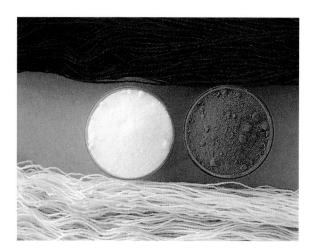

For madder dyeing on wool yarn or cloth, only alum is required as a mordant.

For madder dyeing on cotton yarn or cloth a number of various mordant components are used, including Turkey red oil, alum, chalk, lime, and tannin (gall nut).

Red Dyes with Madder
Main Recipe
(According to Sandberg & Sisefsky, 1982)

Ingredients	a.	b.	c.
Yarn (wool)	100 g	100 g	100 g
Madder	25 g	50 g	100 g
Alum	20 g	25 g	30 g
(Wine stone)	(5 g)	(5 g)	(5 g)
Water (soft)	5 l	5 l	5 l

Mordanting

The yarn is mordanted in alum (and possibly wine stone) for 60-90 minutes at 90°C. It is advantageous for the mordanted yarn to remain in the mordant bath until it cools off or until the next day.

Before dyeing, the mordanted yarn should be rinsed. The remaining wine stone residue makes the red color yellower.

Dyeing

It is a good idea to soak the finely ground madder the day before dyeing.

Pure water (soft) is somewhat warmed up. Madder is added to the bath and the temperature is increased to 60-70°C. Avoid further temperature increase. The bath must not be filtered!

The yarn is well moistened in water (at a temperature you can put your hand in), squeezed out, put down into the bath and treated there for two hours. It should be drawn on rods during the first 10 minutes.

Make sure that the dye bath properly penetrates below the tied places on the yarn skeins.

If you want the clearest possible red color, the bath must be kept at 60-70°C the entire time, instead of the usual 90°C.

The yarn is washed, rinsed, and dried.

Aftertreatment

If dyeing takes place at 70°C or below, the bath may contain a lot of dyestuff. Yarn pre-mordanted with 20 g alum per 100 g yarn can be aftertreated as long as a useable dye remains.

Commentary

The recipe gives a range of red colors with various degrees of saturation. The lighter ones can, as in the case with aftertreatment, become somewhat yellow.

Fastness

Light fastness among red madder dyes at full strength lies at 4-5. More powerful deep red tones can reach up to 6, just like all darkening madder dyes.

With rose dyes, the light fastness sinks to below 4, but does not go as low as corresponding dyes with cochineal.

Madder dyes do not loose clarity with bleaching as many red colored dyewoods do.

Red-Brown to Dark-Brown Colors with Madder
(According to Sandberg & Sisefsky, 1982)

Ingredients	a.	b.	c.
Yarn (wool)	100 g	100 g	100 g
Madder	100 g	100 g	100 g
Alum	30 g	30 g	30 g
(Wine stone)	(5 g)	(5 g)	(5 g)
Blue vitriol	5 g	10 g	20 g
Green vitriol	2 g	5 g	10 g
Tannin (gall nut)	2 g	4 g	8 g
Water (soft)	5 l	5 l	5 l

Mordanting

The yarn is mordanted in alum (and possibly wine stone) for 60-90 minutes at 90°C. It is advantageous to leave the mordanted yarn in the mordant bath until it cools off or until the following day. Then rinse.

Dyeing

Soak the finely ground madder the day before dyeing. For coarsely ground madder, soak several days before use.

The water is heated somewhat. Madder, the blue vitriol, and the tannin (or finely pulverized gall nut) are added to the bath and the temperature is now increased to 70°C.

The yarn is moistened well (in water at a temperature you can put your hand in), squeezed out, and placed in the bath, where it is treated for 45-90 minutes while the temperature is increased to 90°C. It should draw on rods for the first 10 minutes. Make sure that the dye bath penetrates properly under the tied areas on the skeins.

The yarn is lifted up occasionally and green vitriol is added. When it has dissolved, the yarn is dipped again. Dyeing continues for a maximum of 15 minutes after that.

The yarn is washed and rinsed well, the last time in vinegar-acidified water.

Aftertreatment

An afterbath can be used for dyeing alum mordanted yarn. Green and blue vitriol can be added to the bath, but not more than half of the original amounts.

Variations

A number of red colors can be obtained by using a combination of additions to the madder bath as indicated below.

1. Blue vitriol alone gives a warm, red-brown color.

2. Green vitriol and tannin (without copper) give dark (but not as warm) brown tones.

3. Blue vitriol and green vitriol without tannin give brown colors, although not as dark and deep as in the original recipe.

The color scale of 1-3 can be increased further by aftertreatment with potash or ammonium hydrate.

"Rödskivig kanelspindling" (red gilled cinnamon spindle) from Ovansjö parish, Gästrikland.

Red Textile Colors in Mushrooms

It is a peculiar fact that mushrooms for textile dyeing purposes were first discovered in our times. European literature does not make any references to red dye mushrooms, raising doubts about whether our extensive dyeing history that covers many millennia is really as well documented as we believe. It would be strange if these interesting and worthwhile dye plants did not attract attention, especially if they show off their dyestuff in an otherwise uncommon manner.

During the second world war the dyestuff in mushrooms was of interest to chemists, but it wasn't until 1974 that the possibilities of mushrooms became known among dyers through the work of Miriam Rice.

In Sweden there are primarily two types of the family *Dermocybe* that produce good red colors, *D. sanguinea* "blodröd kanelspindling" ("blood red cinnamon spindle") and *D. semisanguinea* "rödskivig kanelspindling" (red gilled cinnamon spindle). Each contain several different anthraquinone dyestuffs (primarily dermocybin) and in this they resemble madder and cochineal both technically and coloristically. *D. sanguinea* can yield as much as 15 percent dyestuff in dry weight while *D. semisanguinea* gives approximately one-fifth of that (only the caps) but is significantly easier to find.

Wool is dyed in the same manner as with other plant dyes. The yarn can be pre-mordanted with alum, tin salt, or potassium dichromate Tin gives the most colorful dyes, almost like cochineal and chrome, unclear with a tinge of violet. It is preferable to prepare the dyebath using dried and pulverized material that may remain in the bath during dyeing.

The light fastness resembles what corresponding dyes obtain with madder or cochineal (close to 5 for the most powerfully colored dyes and higher with chrome mordant).

Mushroom Dyeing – Some Practical Advice

The dye content of mushrooms often varies depending on ripeness, time of year, and growing areas. As with other plant dyes, some of the mushroom dyes are more or less sensitive to the quality of the water. For this reason, working with soft water and a pre-mordanted yarn is usually recommended.

For pre-mordanting wool material, yarn, or loose wool, use 3-5 liters of water with the following added ingredients to 100 g yarn:

    alum - 25 g and 10 g wine stone

    tin salt - 3 g and 20 g wine stone (treatment time about 20 minutes)

    blue vitriol (copper sulfate) - 15 g

    green vitriol (iron sulfate) - 15-25 g and 5 g wine stone and 30 g of Glauber's salt

Start the mordanting at 40°C and increase gradually to 90°C where the treatment will take place for about an hour

Dermocybin

Which Colors Do We Get with the Above Mordants?

"Blodröd kanelspindling" (Blood red cinnamon spindle)

unmordanted	brown-orange
alum	red
tin	red
copper	brown-red
iron	purple-black

"Rödskivig kanelspindling" (Red gilled cinnamon spindle)

unmordanted	brown-orange
alum	red
tin	orange-red
copper	brown-red
iron	purple-black

For the person who wants to go into more depth in this interesting form of plant dyeing, several excellent books by Carla and Erik Sundström are recommended: *Färga med svampar (Dyeing with Mushrooms)* and *Skapa av växtfärgat garn (Creating with Plant-Dyed Yarn)*.

Environmental Aspects of Dyeing With Natural Dyestuffs

The dyestuffs that are used in the sample recipes in this book, madder and cochineal, do not contain any elements that are harmful to the environment. The same is probably the case for the textile assistants, tannin, olive oil, etc.

Only the metals used in mordanting can be a potential risk factor when released in nature. Aluminum (from alum), iron, copper, and tin are used in these recipes. The metals released by natural dyers are of course extremely insignificant compared to industry, even if the latter were maximizing the cleanup of their discharge.

These metals already exist in nature and can neither be created or totally destroyed. In nature they exist in an insoluble form, and damage to animals and plants rarely occurs near bodies of ore. Local damage is seen only in areas where large quantities of metals are released in a water-soluble form.

In a dye or mordant bath, the amount of mordant used is calculated according to the quantity of goods. Once the process is complete, it is nearly impoverished of metal salts. The main thing a dyer can do to eliminate any remaining loose metals in the used bath is to combine them with alkali (common washing soda). The metals then form insoluble hydroxides that will later, for the most part, be converted to oxides that are even harder to dissolve. It is possible to check whether the alkalinity of the discharge is greater than nine with pH paper.

An additional protective measure is to collect all the discharge in concrete vats filled with gravel. These should be open so that the water can evaporate, but protected against acid rain with a roof. All chemical reactions that can occur when mixing the various residue baths lead to increasingly insoluble residue products (mineralization).

Dyers should make sure that the majority of the metals used are fixed to the dyed products. Through wear or by discarding them, they return to nature in an insoluble oxide form, and are spread over such a large area that no risks exist. Even industry primarily uses dyes that attach to the fiber with the help of metals that return to the environment in the same manner.

Aluminum is one of the most common metals on earth and is found in the majority of the earth's minerals in the form of silicates (clay and feldspar), but also as hydroxides and oxides. The reason that loose aluminum becomes a risk factor is because of the acid breakdown that releases aluminum from common feldspar. Acid breakdown occurs when the sulfurous content of fossil fuel is used. The proper preventative measure is exhaust emission control, not a reduction in the release of alum in the used mordant bath.

Iron is the most common metal on earth and it also exists as a natural ingredient in human blood. An adult has several grams of iron in their body in this form. Iron released in ground water is generally not a risk factor of any significance. In nature iron mainly occurs as oxides and hydroxides.

Copper also occurs in the body as a natural trace element but in significantly smaller amounts. The cases of damage by copper that have been reported are the result of water pipes being attacked by acidic water. In nature, copper is mainly found in the form of sulfides and oxides.

Tin is a typical heavy metal and should be the greatest potential risk factor among those listed. Damage by tin is seldom reported, probably because it is hard to keep in solution and returns to an insoluble form more quickly than other metals. The most common form of the tin mineral is the oxide (tinstone).

Picture weave by Kerstin Gustafsson, 90 x 90 cm. The yarns are mushroom dyed with "Blodröd kanelspindling" (blood red cinnamon spindle), "Rödskivig kanelspindling" (red gilled cinnamon spindle), and "lysticka" (lysticka, a species of Polyporus or shelf bracket fungus which often grows on trees or logs).

THE CHEMISTRY OF THE NATURAL RED DYES

Jan Sisefsky

When a chemist goes to work with a previously unknown substance, the first step is to produce an analysis. The small parts of the substance — the molecules — consist of various types of atoms, and the first step is to determine which atoms they are and in what proportions they exist. In the case of very simple substances, such an analysis can go far, but when the element comes from the plant or animal kingdom, it often has such a complicated structure that is necessary to determine the order in which the various atoms are bound to each other. Such a structural analysis then allows far-reaching conclusions to be drawn about the properties of the substance and the possibilities for its use.

Modern Research Concerning Purple

Can Chemists Solve the Mystery?

Today such a task is relatively simple, but when Paul Friedländer took on purple dyestuff in 1906, chemistry as a science had barely developed far enough for such a task to be within the realm of possibility.

Significantly larger quantities of the substance were necessary for doing the analysis than is the case today. From various zoological stations in the Mediterranean, Friedländer collected 12,000 samples of *Murex (Bolinus) brandaris*, and was successful in extracting 1.4 grams of purple dyestuff from them — barely enough for such an analysis. In some ways the results are sensational: The purple dyestuff turned out to be nearly identical to the indigo dyestuff. Only in two places in the molecule was a hydrogen atom replaced by a bromine atom! The relationship between two dyestuffs that came from such completely different organisms was astounding. Not long after the analysis was completed, a synthesis was done, constructing a synthetic purple dyestuff with exactly the same properties as the natural ones from simpler chemical substances.

Cis   *Trans*

The figure shows the most common method for schematically showing the structural formula of the purple dyestuff. Every point where two lines join contains a carbon atom, and a hydrogen atom is attached to every available position on the carbons that does not have another element attached to it. N indicates a nitrogen atom, O indicates an oxygen atom, and Br indicates a bromine atom. The single and double lines indicate the types of bonds that attach the elements' electrons. The large circles indicate a special bonding type between six carbons that are very close together in a flat configuration (benzene ring). Otherwise, the figure does not give any indication of the size and distance between the atoms, nor does it show how the molecule looks in three dimensions.

Has our mystery now been solved with this chemical achievement? Friedländer himself did not think so. Was this unclear blue-red color really the one that the ancient people called dazzling purple red, that the emperors and courtesans in the past paid fortunes to be able to wear? Did other types of purple mollusks hide other secrets?

At least one such secret has been uncovered in our times by Irving Ziderman at the Israel Fibre Institute in Jerusalem. He discovered that another common purple mollusk, *Murex (Truncularioptis) trunculus*, contains nearly equal amounts of Friedländer's dibromine indigo (6,6-dibromoindigotin) and common indigo (indigotin), the latter of which is exactly the same dyestuff as in the various indigo plants (ref. D). This mollusk gives an even bluer color than *Murex brandaris*. This discovery may explain references by the ancient writers to "common" or red-purple and to blue-purple.

Nowadays we have a good overview of the structure of the original prestage of the purple dyestuff that is produced by the mollusk, and the various stages that lead to the finished dyestuff. Many older authors (including Goethe) have described the various color changes that accompany these conversions. Already in the story from the Apocrypha, which is retold on page 24, we notice that the shepherd, when he dried the mollusk secretion off of the dog's nose with a piece of wool, did not immediately observe anything strange. Not until the wool was put in the sunlight did a color change occur that surprised him just as much as it did the spectators.

(S = Sulfur atom)

The First Purple Prestage

It is no coincidence that Ziderman works in Israel. One of the colors mentioned in the bible with the ceremonial meaning *tekhelet* can now with the greatest probability be identified as the blue purple. Because The Lord in the bible requires his believers to wear tassels in the corner of their prayer shawl with a thread of *tekhelet* tied in, it is important for many religious Jews to be able to follow this command literally (ref. C). This has not been possible for fourteen hundred years, despite endless speculation about what *tekhelet* was and what the color looked like. Luther even believed that it was yellow because of mistaken associations with the word *hyacinthina*. Only with Ziderman's research efforts is it now possible to renew this custom. The research that will be undertaken as a result of this effort will hopefully solve the remaining mysteries surrounding this antique dyestuff.

The considerable similarities between indigo and the purple dyestuffs make it possible to speculate about what to do when dyeing with purple and how to control the result of a dyeing to help reach the desired color.

With both indigo and purple two principally separate possibilities exist for getting the dye to absorb and fix itself to a textile fiber. In the first one the prestage is water-soluble. It can be absorbed by a textile fiber and subsequently converted to the insoluble dyestuff which can not be removed by any normal washing process. In the second, the dyestuff can be dissolved in water after forming by the use of a special chemical process, pre-vatting. A reducing agent in alkaline solution converts the dyestuff to a soluble form (leuco form) which has a completely different and lighter color than the dyestuff itself.

Leuco Dibromine Indigo

Leuco Dibromine Indigo

When the leuco form has absorbed into the fiber, the dyestuff is reformed by lifting the textile material out of the dyebath and subjecting it to acid in the air. Many think that the soluble prestages of both indigo and dibromine indigo are identical to the leuco forms, but this is not the case. There can be great differences in how quickly they are absorbed and oxidize, and only experience can determine the advantages and disadvantages of the various methods.

With indigo, literature sometimes indicates that the former method was used in primitive cases, but it is less suitable because the prestage quickly oxidizes to indigo in the dye bath, making it lost to the textile material. The norm was (and is) to dye from vats. Literature gives numerous examples of

how dyers understood early on the method for producing the necessary chemical reduction, using sugar-containing agents that fermented in water that was made alkaline with lime. It was also possible to use urine, where both reducing agents and the necessary alkali (ammonium hydrate) were formed during the fermentation process. The urine vat is easier to operate and more beautiful on a wool fiber, but difficult to produce on a large scale, so urine is usually only used as a smaller addition in the first type of fermentation vat.

The scarce and obscure literary references to purple dyeing suggest that it was normal to start from the dyestuff prestage, which turned out to be significantly more stable than the corresponding one with indigo (ref. B). Namely, strong light is needed to oxidize to purple, while the indigo prestage is converted to indigo even in the dark.

The mention of urine by some of the authors is the only thing that can be interpreted as alluding to the actual vat process, but on the other hand it was common to use urine as a dyeing assistant in a number of other connections, above all in the production of ochril preparation by which purple was falsified. (See page 35 for purple dyeing techniques.)

The numerous literary references to purple being red or light red have given rise to a number of speculations about how it might be able to produce a redder mollusk color — perhaps a color similar to the purple color used in heraldry. Again it is possible to draw conclusions based on indigo. It is known that certain indigo-producing plants also form a chemically similar red dye (indirubin), in which the molecular components are put together in another manner.

Indirubin

Indirubin

It has been suggested that indirubin might be found with purple dyed material, perhaps even brominated (ref. E). The difficulty with increasing the redness in the purple color is that it can easily be converted to common indigo tin and dibromine indigo tin respectively when dyeing.

What Friedländer could not determine was whether the structure of both halves of the dibromine indigo molecule were in cis or transforms like figures 1a or 1b. Today we believe that the trans-form is the standard one, but the relationship between them can be influenced both by the circumstances under which the prestage is converted to dibrome indigo and by how the leuco form is re-oxidized. Does this play any role? With indigo it does not seem to make any significant difference, but Christophersen and Wätjen (ref. A) have demonstrated that the cis-form is redder than the trans-form of the purple dyestuff. It is possible that the dyers of antiquity understood how to control the process so that the red form was favored.

Once purple dyestuff was successfully produced synthetically (which turned out not to be very attractive in the dye market, despite good fastness qualities), an attempt was made to produce similar dyestuffs with different numbers of bromine atoms and in all other possible places on the molecule. The result was that no other grouping gave a redder dyestuff than the one Friedländer found (ref. F). Most were blue without a trace of redness. Some were used because of their good fastness to light, which even exceeded indigo, including that which is still used today as the standard for light fastness in textile fibers (no. 8 of the so-called blue wool scale).

Is it necessary to dismiss the statements about the beautiful purple as a myth? Most of the textile objects that it has been possible to confirm as having been dyed with mollusk purple alone are about the color that Friedländer obtained, or an even bluer (and in many cases significantly less clear and a browner) color. More beautiful red colors have been produced with other dyestuffs, above all with kermes. With the help of tin mordanting it would have been possible to create colors that can not be exceeded by modern dyestuffs with respect to chroma.

It is actually easier in dyeing to draw the color toward bluer tones than toward redder ones. The leuco form of dibromine indigo easily loses its bromine atoms if vat dyeing is done in the light, and it reforms as common indigo dyestuff (ref. G). *Purpura blatta* can be "converted" to *purpura hyacinthina* with the help of the addition of a common indigo, a "falsification" that even today's chemists would have a hard time exposing. It is highly likely that this method, which made the production of *purpura hyacinthina* significantly cheaper, was known by the dyers of antiquity, even though for obvious reasons the literature does not say anything about it. On the other hand, *purpura hyacinthina* is converted to *purpura blatta* by oxidizing the prestage in the dark, and the precipitated indigo is removed. There are reasons to believe that the expert dyer used this artistic trick of the trade to adjust the mollusk catch to changes in fashion. (ref. B).

The dyers of the old times naturally had no inkling of the chemical sequence that took place in the vat, and their patience and ingenuity must be admired. By trial and error alone they developed such a complicated and difficult dyeing method as the dyeing of purple.

Beautifying Purple with Ochril

Chemical analysis of textiles that were dyed purple using mollusk dyestuff revealed an accompanying ochril residue. Ochril is a beautiful purple dyestuff that is formed by certain kinds of lichen when they are treated with ammonium hydrate, for example in urine. The dyestuff is much more brilliant than mollusk purple, but by comparison it has low light fastness. (See page 40.)

Many explanations have been given for why this combination was used, but the most probable is the one recently advanced by Karen Casselman at the museum in Nova Scotia. A newly produced garment sparkled in the most beautiful red violet color. After a while the ochril color looked more or less bleached, but the garment did not turn gray like it would have been if ochril alone had been used; instead it became a more brilliant and perhaps also a bluer color. People did not notice this gradual change as easily.

Ochril does not need to have been added by overdyeing, rather if you assume that some form of fermentation vat with ammonium hydrate from urine is used for dyeing with mollusk purple, *Rocella*-lichen can be directly added to this vat and this forms ochril, which also is absorbed at the same temperature (about 40°C). It is also possible that the fermentation process in the vat is promoted by the carbohydrate content of the lichen.

(A) Christophersen, C. & Wätjen, F. Purpur. *Naturens Verden* 326 (1978). (Purple. The World of Nature).

(B) McGovern, P.E. & Michel R.H. "Royal Purple and the Phoenician Dye Industry of Lebanon", *MASCA Journal* 3, no. 3 (1984).

(C) Zinderman, I.I. "Blue thread of the Tzitzit; Was the Ancient Dye a Prussian Blue or Tyrian Purple?", *Journal Soc Dyers and Colorists* 97, no. 8, (1981).

(D) Zinderman, I.I. "3600 Years of Purple-Shell Dyeing: Characterization of Hyacinthine Purple (*tekhelet*)", Advances in Chemistry Series 212. American Chemical Society, Washington, (1986).

(E) *Colour Index*. The Society of Dyers and Colourists.

(F) Cyrén, O. Syntetiska *Färgämnen Och Läkemedel* (1939) (Synthetic Dyestuff and Medicines).

(G) Schweppe, H. Undtersuchung alter Textilfärbungen die BASF (June, 1976).

The figures show the structural formulas for the three most important scale insect dyes, carminic acid (cochineal), kermesic acid (kermes), and laccaic acid (*lacdye*). As can be seen, madder dyestuffs and red mushroom dyestuff (see page 182) are related because they are anthraquinone dyestuffs. The difference is that in the former only a few hydrogen atoms are replaced by other groups, while almost all empty spaces in the molecule here contain various groups, OH^-, CH_3^-, and others. Laccaic acid also has complicated side chains containing an amino group (NH) consisting of a nitrogen and a hydrogen, a unique absorption material among natural anthraquinone dyestuffs. Note the commonly occurring $COOH^-$ groups which make the dyestuff acidic.

When the dyestuffs are dissolved in water they release some of the positive hydrogen ions while the remainder of the dyestuff forms negatively charged ions. These remain in dynamic equilibrium with the unionized dyestuff molecules, so that they spend part of their time in ionized form and the remainder in unionized form. The addition of acid to the dye bath shift that equilibrium so that absorption of the dyestuff on the fiber is promoted.

Just like the dyestuffs in the plants, the scale insect dyestuffs exist originally in the form of glycosides, that is, they are bound to various types of sugars. These sugars, which are usually split off during dyeing or producing dyestuff in pure form, are not shown in the structured formulas.

Karminsyra

Kermesinsyra

Laccainsyra

Anthraquinone

Plant-dyed yarns for production of pile rugs, Anatolia.

The Chemistry of Madder Dyestuffs

Figures 1-5 show the structural formulas of some of the most important dyestuffs from the roots of various types of *Rubiacae*. It is clear that these are also anthraquinone dyestuffs, even though the majority have less complicated structures than the dyes in the cochineal group and the red dyeing "kanelspindlingarna" (the cinnamon spindles). (See page 182.) As a natural dye in general, these have coupled to one or more types of sugar that help them to dissolve in the dye bath (not shown in the figures). Everything indicates that these types of sugars generally split off when the dyestuff fixes itself to the mordant and via that to the fiber. They can therefore contribute to the dyeing sequence, but not to the dye's fastness and other qualities once they are fixed to the textile material.

Figure 6 is one of the structures suggested for Turkey red (K. Venkataraman: *The Chemistry of Synthetic Dyes*, Vol II. Academic Press, New York 1952). Only alizarin fits into that complex so that the attempts that have been made to produce similar dyeings with cochineal or madder dye where alizarin is missing must have the prerequisite that the dyestuff breaks down to alizarin (if possible) in order for the dye to get the desired qualities associated with a genuine Turkey red. In addition, it is possible to see that oil or any residue of it does not enter into the final dyestuff molecule.

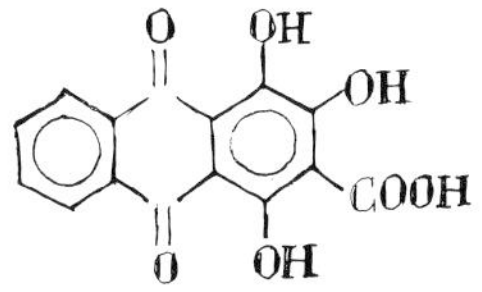

1. Pseudopurpurin

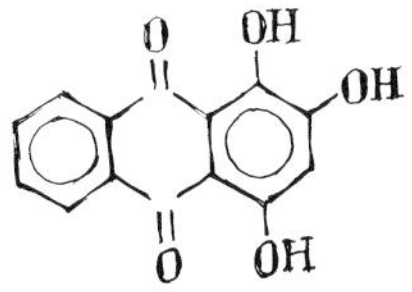

2. Purpurin

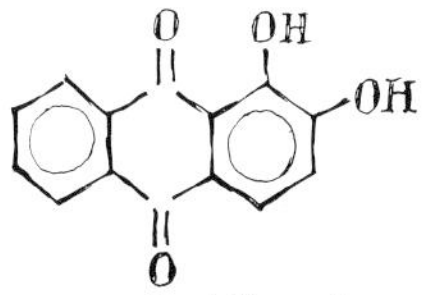

3. Alizarin

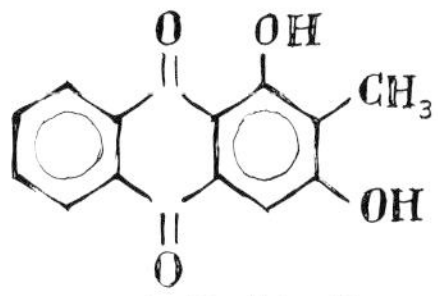

4. Rubiadin

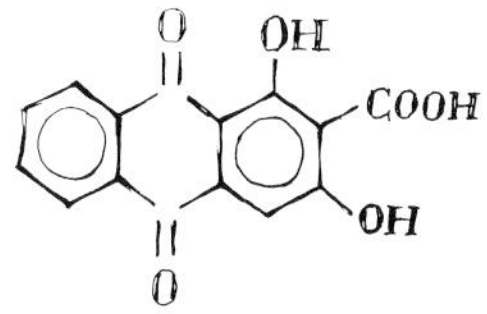

5. Munjistin

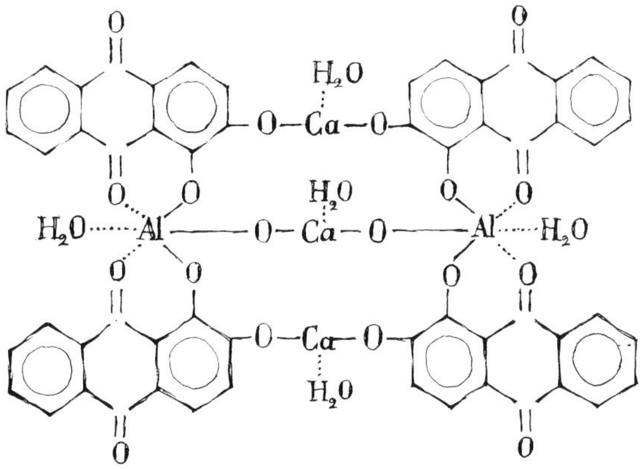

6. Turkey red

From the Odyssey, *by Homer*

Odysseus and Nausikaa

Straight rose the lovely Morne, that up did raise
Faire-veild Nausicaa, whose dreame her praise
To Admiration tooke. Who no time spent
To give the rapture of her vision vent
To her lov'd parents, whome she found within,
Her mother set at fire, who had to spin
A Rocke, whose tincture with sea-purple shin'd,
Her maids about her. But she chanc't to find
Her Father going abroad, to Counsell calld
By his grave Senate.

Homer, the author of Greece's classic epos
the *Iliad* and the *Odyssey,* probably from the 700s B.C.

—(*Chapman's Homer*. Volume Two. Translated by
George Chapman. Princeton University Press,
Princeton, New Jersey: 1956.)

Some of the documents from the author's book collection from which material was obtained to write this book.

Sources and Literature

The number of publications from which inspiration, factual information, and excerpts have been obtained is so great that a complete list would be way too extensive and require too much space. This bibliography is therefore highly limited and mainly covers a number of more significant works on the subject and the works that have been referenced in the text. This does not cover, for reasons given above, the trade journals, essays, etc. that have also been valuable sources of information. On the other hand, the list is complemented with a number of works that are recommended as supplementary reading (marked with *).

Adrosko, Rita J. *Natural Dyes and Home Dyeing.* New York: 1971.

Allgemeines Handbuch für Callico-, Cambric-, Siz-, Kattun-, und Leinwanddrucker. Bearb. von S.F. Hermbstedt. Leipzig: 1805.

Beckmann, John. *A History of Inventions, Discoveries \ and Origins,* (Kermes-Koschenill). London: 1846 (repr. Amsterdam: 1974).

Berthollet, C. L. *Elements de l'art de la Teinture.* Paris: 1791.

Bindewald, E. *Bunter Traum auf Gewebtem Grund.* Braunschweig: 1950.*

Bird, C. L. *The Theory and Practice of Wool Dyeing.* SDC. Bradford: 1947.

Blumer, Ferdinand. *Anfang und frühe Entwicklung des Zeugdrucks in der Schweiz unter besonderer Berücksichtigung des Kantons Glarus.* Schwanden: no date.

Boger, Gustaf. Väsgötaknallarna. 1963. The peddlars from Västergötland.

Boyle, Robert. *Experimenta et Considerationes de Coloribus.* Rotterdam, 1671.

Bühler, Alfred. *Ikat, Batik, Plangi.* Basel: 1972.

Bühler, Alfred and E. Fisher. *Musterung von Stoffen mit Hilfe von Presschablonen.* Basel: 1974.*

Bürgin, Alfred. *Geshichte des Geigy-Unternehmens 1758-1939.*

Canáls y Marti, J. P. *Coleccion de lo Perteneciente al Ramo De la Rubia ó Granza, en España.* Madrid: 1779.

Colour Index. The Society of Dyers and Colourists. Bradford: 1971.

Davatz, Jürg. *"Hänggitürme" im Glarnerland.* Glarus: 1986.

Diderot and d'Alembert. *Encyclopédie ou Dictionnaire raisonné des sciences, des arts et des metiers.* Paris: 1751.

Donkin, R. A. *"Spanish Red," an Ethnographical Study of Cochineal and the Opuntia Cactus.* Cambridge: 1977.

En upriktig och pålitelig färge-bok. Stockholm: 1759. A straightforward and reliable dyebook.

Fachwörterbuch für die Farbstoffe und Textilhilfsmittel. New York: 1947.

Fataburen. Nordiska Museets och Skansens årsbok, 1918 och 1960. Fataburen: the Annual of the Nordiska Museum and Skansen 1918 and 1960.

Fernandez, L. *Arte de la Tintura.* Madrid: 1778.

Franzén, A. M. and Nockert, M. *Bonaderna från Skog och Överhogdal.* Stockholm: 1992. Hanging tapestries from Skog and Överhogdal.

Freuler, Kasper. *Aus der Geschichte des Glarnerischen Zeugdrucks.* Freulerpalats, Näfels: no date.

Fuchs, L. *Läbliche Abbildung und Contrafaytung aller Kreüter*. Basel: 1545.

Förädlad Textil. Borås: 1951. Processed Textiles.

Gadd, P.A. *Underrättelse om Färgestofters planteringar i Finland af Saflor, Krapp och Vau*. Åbo: 1760. Information on the planting of safflower, madder, and weld in Finland.

Garmo, S. *Rättviksdräkten*. Malung: 1986. Costumes from Rättivik.

Geijer, Agnes. *Ur textilkonstens historia*. Lund: 1980.* From the history of textile art.

Gittenger, M. *Master-Dyers of the World*. Washington: 1982.*

—-. *Splendid Symbols*. Washington: 1979.*

Handel and Industrie des Kantons Glarus. A. Jenny-Trümpy, 1903.

Hellot, Jean. *L'Art de la Teinture*. Paris: 1750.

Henschen, Ingegerd. *Kattuntryck, Svenskt tygtryck 1720-1850*. Stockholm: 1992. Calico Print, Swedish cloth print, 1720-1850.

—-. *Tygtryck i Sverige* (före 1700). Stockholm: 1942. Cloth print in Sweden (before 1700).

Herbarium Mathiolo Camerariani. Prag: 1596.

Hermbstedt, S. F. *Magazin für Färber, Zeugdrucker und Bleicher*. Berlin: 1804 och 1811.

Horsfall, R. S. and L. G. Lawrie. *The Dyeing of Textile Fibres*. London: 1927.

Hölterhoffs, G. W. *Handbuch der Kunst-Färberei*. Erfurt: 1809.

Ibn Battuta. *Reisen ans Ends der Welt*. Stuttgart: 1985.

Indigo Rein. BASF. Ludwigshafen: 1907.

James, E. O. *Gravarna berättar*. Stockholm: 1986. The tombs/graves tell.

—-. *Prehistoric Religion*. London: 1867.

Jeffreys, J. G. *The Mollusca*. London: 1867.

Kindlimann, Heinz. *150 Jahre Glarner Zeugdruck*. Schwanden: 1978.

Kirschbaum, R. *Indiennes, exotische Kattundruck in der Schweiz*. 1987.

Koch, J.H. *Mit Model, Krapp und Indigo*. Hamburg: 1984.

Koctürk-Runefors, Tahire. *En fråga om heder*. Otta: 1991.* A matter of honor/honesty.

Krähenbühl, E. A. *Der Zeugdruck*. Basel: 1951.

Landolt-Tüller, A. & H. *Qalamkar-Druck in Isfahan*. Basel: 1976.

Lexikon der Farben-Technik. Berch, J. Berlin: 1903.

Lindqvist, Cecilia. *Tecknens Rike*. Stockholm: 1989.* The empire of signs/symbols (Chinese characters).

Macquer, P. J. *Die Kunst der Seidenfärberei*. Leipzig: 1764.

Marco Polos resor. (revised by B. Thordeman). Helsingfors: 1944. The Travels of Marco Polo.

Mattsson, Axel. *Plinius den yngres brev*. Liber: 1984. Letters of Pliny the Younger.

Mellaart, J. *Çatal Hüyük, A Neolithic Town in Anatolia*. Adenau: 1989.

Mendes de Costa, E. *The Shells of Great Britain and Ireland*. London: 1778.

Moberg, C-A. *Överhogdalstapetens livsträd*. 1925.* The tree of life in Överhogoal's Tapestry.

Nabholz-Kartasccoff, M-L. *Golden Sprays and Scarlet Flowers, Traditional Indian Textiles*. Kyoto.

Nuttall, Zelia. Putnam Anniversary Volume *"Anthropological Essays."* New York: 1909.

Osbeck, Pehr. *Dagbok över en Ostindisk Resa, åren 1750, 1751, 1752.* Stockholm: 1757. Diary of a trip to the East Indies in 1750, 1751, 1752.

Otavsky, Karel: *Alte Gewebe und Ihre Geschichte.* Riggisberg: 1987.

Packer, Th. *Handbok för färgare.* Stockholm: 1840. Handbook for Dyers.

—. *The Dyers Guide.* London: 1816.

Papyrus Graecus Holmiensis (revised by O. Lagercrantz). Uppsala & Leipzig: 1913.

Persian Printed Cotton (intr. J. M. Wearden). London: 1989.

Persoz, J. *Traité Théorique et Pratique de l'impression des Tissus.* Paris: 1846.

Plinii, Caii Secundi. *Historiae Naturalis.* Parisiis: 1779.

Pliny. *Natural History* (translated by H. Rackham). Harvard U. Press, 1938.

Ploss, E. E. *Ein Buch von Alten Farben.* Heidelberg/Berlin: 1962.*

Poezija Narodnogo Kostjuma. Mertsalova, M. N. Moskva: 1988.

Popstefanieva, Maritza. *Makedonski Narondni Vezovi.* Skopje, 1953.

Real-Enzyklopädie der Gesamten Pharmazie. Berlin/Wein: 1904-1912.

Rice, Miriam. *Mushrooms for Color.* Eureka, ca1980.

Rosander, G. *Herrarbete, dalfolkets säsongvisa arbetsvandringar.* Uppsala, 1967.* Mens' work, the seasonal employment migrations of the people from Dalarna.

Rosetti, G. V. *Plictho de Larte de Tentori.* Venedig, 1540/1548.

—. *Facsimile of 1548 Edition.* New York: 1968.

Rubruk, Vilhelm av. *Resa genom Asien (1253-1255).* 1986.* A trip through Asia (1253-1255).

Runge, Ferdinand. *Technische Chemi, del 1 & 2.* Berlin: 1838/39.

Russian Kerchiefs and Shawls. Leningrad: 1985.

Ryder, L. M. *The Evolution of the Fleece.* S. Am.: Jan. 1987.

Ryhiner, Jean. *Traité sur la Fabrication et la Commerce des Toiles Peintes, Commencé en 1766.*

Sahlin, C. *Ett skånskt fargeri.* Stockholm: 1928. A dyeworks in Skane.

Salmon, T. H. *Hedendaagsche Historie, of Tegenwoordige Staat van alle Volkeren.* Amsterdam: 1731.

Sandberg, Gösta. *Batik* (second edition). Stockholm: 1972.

—. *De turkröda kattuntrycken i Dalarnas dräktskick.* (Dalarnas Hembygdsbok). 1989. The Turkey red calicos in the costume customs of Dalarna.

—. *Ikat.* Stockholm: 1984.

—. *Indigo—en bok om blå textilier.* Stockholm: 1986. Indigo: a book about blue textiles.

—. *Indigo Textiles: Technique and History.* A & C Black, London. Lark Books, Asheville, North Carolina: 1989.

Sandberg, Gösta and J. Sisefsky. Växtfärgning (5:e uppl). Stokholm: 1982. Plant dyeing (5th edition).

Scützenberger and H. Schröder. *Die Farbstoffe,* parts 1 & 2. Berlin: 1873.

Sockendräkter i Dalarna. Dalarnas Fornminnes och Hembygdsförbunds skriftserie. 1976. Parish Costumes in Dalarna. A publication in the series on Dalarna's ancient monuments and native district association.

Sterner, Björn. *Bygdeknallar och stadsköpmän.* Stockholm. Country peddlars and city merchants.

Stüssi, H. *Lockender Orient—Conrad Blumers grosse Reise ("Neujahrsbote Glarner Hinterland" 1988).*

Sulzer, Klaus. *Vom Zeugdruck zur Rotfärberei.* Zurich: 1991.

Sundström, Carla and Erik. *Färga med svampar.* Västerås: 1983. Dye with mushrooms.

Svensk Flora. Carl von Linné. Stockholm: 1986. Translated and corrected edition of *Flora Svecica*, published by Lars Salvius in 1755.

Textile Collections of the World. Edited by Cecil Lubell. Volume 1: USA and Canada, 2: England and Ireland, 3: Frankrike. Studio Vista, London: 1976.*

The Dyers Art. Larsen, J. L. New York: 1976.

The Fabrics of Mulhouse and Alsace 1750-1800. Leigh-on-Sea: 1968.

Thompson, Jon. *Orientmattans underbara värld.* (original English title: *Carpets from the Tents, Cottages and Workshops of Asia.* London: 1988). Borås: 1989.* The wonderful world of Oriental rugs.

Thunberg, C. P. *Resa uti Europa, Africa, Asia. . .* Uppsala: 1788. Travels in Europe, Africa, Asia. . .

Tomita, Jun and Noriko. *Japanese Ikat Weaving.* London: 1982.

Uhlig, Helmut. *Die Mutter Europas.* Bergisch Gladbach, 1991.

Warren-Lexikon für Chemikalien and Drogen. Meissen: 1920.

Warg, Cajsa. *Hjelpreda I Hushållningen for Unga Fruentimber.* 3: e uppl. Stockholm, 1762, 9: e uppl. Tilökt med en Färgbok, 1790. Housekeeping guide book for young women. 3rd edition: Stockholm, 1792, 9th edition: enlarged with a dye book, 1790.

Varulexikon (Illustreradt). Stockholm: 1894. Product Encyclopedia (Illustrated).

Westring, J. P. *Svenska Lafvarnas Färghistoria.* Stockholm: 1805. The history of Swedish lichen.

Additional Sources

Conversations and letter exchanges with the following persons contributed invaluable information to this book.

Amanuens Salih Abdulhak, Naroden Museij, Ohrid, Macedonia.

Master Dyer Dorje Anastasovski, Lazaropolje, Macedonia.

Engineer Ernst Blumer, Ennenda, Glarus.

Textile Researcher Karen Casselman, Nova Scotia.

Dr. Jürg Davatz, Museum des Landes Glarus, Näfels, GL.

Dr. Albert Diener, Landesarchiv des Kantons Glarus, GL.

Dr. Herbert Fritsche-Herzog, Zollikon, ZH.

Textile Artist Kerstin Gustafsson, Rävlanda.

Dir. Liem Koen Hong, Bandung, Java.

Archivists France & Marta Ivansek, Ljubljana.

President Hans Jossi, Greuterhof, Islikon, TG.

Dr. J. H. Koch, Neustadt in Holstein.

Brigitte Kremb, Malmö.

Dr. Jaap Kunst, Tropenmuseum, Amsterdam.

Curator Sanja Lasarevic, Ethnografisk Museij, Zagreb.

Author Dorothy Miller, Santa Cruz, California.

Prof. Maritza Popstefanieva, Ohrid, Macedonia.

Director August Strauch-Weinmann, Zürich.

Dr. K.R.T., Tirtodiningrat, Djogakarta, Java.

Mrs. Slavka Zarceva, Ohrid, Macedonia.

Red Textiles – Where?

For those readers of the book who wish to expand their knowledge of red textiles, or perhaps wish to possess some, a small selection of museums, collections, and places for purchase are recommended here.

Dalarna's Museum, Falun.
Costume collection including plangi-patterned scarves and Turkey red dyed calico prints.

Ethnographic Museum, Göteborg.
Rich collection of ikat, plangi, and batik from the far area of Asia and a large collection of Peruvian textiles.

Kulturen, Lund.
Costumes from southern Sweden and a collection of embroidered costumes and parts of costumes from Macedonia.

Röhsska Konstslöjdmuseet, Göteborg.
Art handcrafts and the art industry, East Asiatic art, and resist techniques and finds from the Fustat graves.

TextilMuseet, Borås.
New textile museum housed in buildings that are interesting in terms of industrial history.

The Sandberg Textile Collection, Nora.
Textiles, tools, and a collection of books about dyeing and printing.

Musée de l'Impression sur Etoffes, Mulhouse, France. Special Museum for Cloth Print and Printing Technology.
The interior has patterns and sample collections from the introductory stages of Turkey red calico printing.

Muséum des Landes Galrus, Freulerpalats, Näfels, Switzerland.
Newly opened department that shows the Swiss calico print production in the canton of Glarus including pattern, print blocks, and models of hanging towers.

Musée des Indiennes, Colombier, Switzerland.
Rich collection of pattern sheets and prints from Indienne manufacturing in the canton of Neuchâtel.

Royal Scottish Museum, Edinburgh, Scotland.
Two hundred folders with pattern samples from the United Turkey Red Company, covering the 1830-1930 period, that are among the most valuable collections at the museum.

Victoria & Albert Museum, London, England.
The Indian Section will be particularly interesting to the readers of this book. It includes one of the world's best collections of Indian calicos, which were brought to Europe by the East India Company.

Stadhuis Museum, Zieriksee, Holland.
The little town once became rich from the madder trade. A section of the museum also throws light on the significant madder cultivation era in Zeeland that is described in the book.

The Textile Museum, Washington D.C., U.S.A.
The only museum in North America and one of the few in the world that specializes in the textiles of ancient times, It includes large Peruvian and Egyptian collections.

Calico Museum of Textiles, Ahmadabad, India.
Extensive and interesting collections of ancient calico prints (chintzes) from various areas of India.

Naroden Museij, Skopje, Macedonia.
Extensive collections of embroidered costumes and related items (calicos, silver jewels, etc.) from the various regions in Macedonia.

Stiftelsen Afroart, Stockholm.
The shop of Folkens Museum, Stockholm, sells resist patterned and printed textiles from various cultural areas.

J.P. Willborg Antika Mattor (J.P. Willborg, Antique Rugs), Stockholm.
Exhibitions and sales of weaves from Anatolia, Persia, Peru, etc. and utilitarian textiles from Skåne.

Jobs Handtryk, Leksand.
Sales of reprinted older Turkey red calicos found in Dalarna, among other things.

Ljungbergs Textiltryck AB, Floda.
Reprints of older Turkey red calicos found in Dalarna.

Glossary

Avivage. A process of treating dyed material in a boiling soap solution to produce hardier dyes with greater chroma.

Batik. East Asiatic method for putting patterns on cloth through wax resist and dyeing.

Beautifying. Involves subjecting an already dyed cloth to a color enhancing final bath.

Dibromine indigo. The active substance in the Tyrian purple of antiquity.

Mix dye. Temporary dye additive (without fastness) to be able to control the placement and quality of a stamp print. It is completely removed from the finished product.

Mordant dyestuff. Water-soluble textile dyestuffs that call for a mordant (usually metal salt) to fix itself to a textile fiber.

Oxidation. In dyeing terminology, bringing a product in contact with the acid in the air.

Plangi. Tie-dye batik.

Pre-vatting. Conversion of a dye (such as indigo) to a soluble form through appropriate additions.

Rouleaux print machine. The same as a roller printing machine.

Stencil print. A form of cloth print where a dye or resist paste is applied to the cloth through leather or paper shablon stencils with pattern details that have been cut out.

Tjanting. Tool for applying wax resist on a batik work.

Vat dyes. A textile dyestuff that is insoluble in water is subject to alkaline influence (reduction) and chemically converted to a water-soluble form.

Weighing down. Adding cheap materials to raw dyestuff (dried cochineal) to make it heavier to secure a higher price.

Pages from L. Fuchs flora, *printed in Basel in 1545. The drawings show wild and cultivated madder.*

Photo Credits

Textile Materials

The majority of the textiles, fragments, print blocks, engravings, etc. that are reproduced in this book are part of Gösta Sandberg's collections. In addition to these, a number of people and institutions have kindly allowed materials to be used for the illustrations in the book.

A.T.A. Stockholm, 24
Sony Berntsson, Rävlanda 90, 93
Dalarnas Museum, Falun 10, 86, 167, 168, 169, 171, 172
Kerstin Gustafsson, Rävlanda 185, 192
Ethnographic Museum, Göteborg 42
Museé de l'Impression sur Etoffes, Mulhouse 136, 145
Ralf Mååg, Insjön 163
Lena Nordström, Stockholm 174
Lena Ringensson, Borås 100
Röhsska Konstslöjdmuseet, Göteborg 116
J.P. Willborg, Stockholm 69

Reconstruction of an Indian print stamp for the production series on page 120 was made by Gunnar Palmgren Grafisk Form.

Photo on page 24 from *Alte Gewebe und ihre Geschichte*. Riggisberg, Switzerland, 1987.

Photographic Materials

All photographs in the book except for those mentioned below were taken by Gösta Sandberg.

Labe Allwin, Stockholm 173
Hj. Dely, Dalarnas Museum, Falun 10, 86, 167, 168, 169, 171, 172
Brigitte Kremb, Malmö 33, 34
Michael Landberg, Nora, has taken the black and white photos in the margins of older copper plate [engravings], steel engravings etc.
National museum, Stockholm 39 (Detail by Cornelius Loos), antique ruins in Palmyra.
Lena Nessle, Sala 8, 18, 26, 27, 31, 73, 87, 111, 113, 130, 132, 136, 146, 148, 149, 154, 156, 164, 165, 166
Lena Ringensson, Borås 91
Erik Sundström, Sandviken, 182

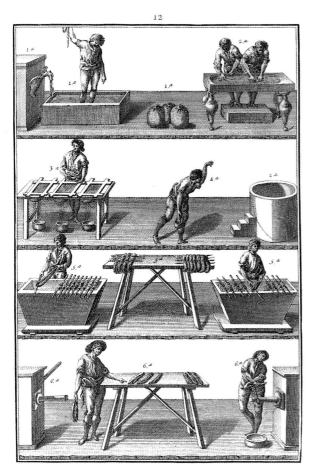

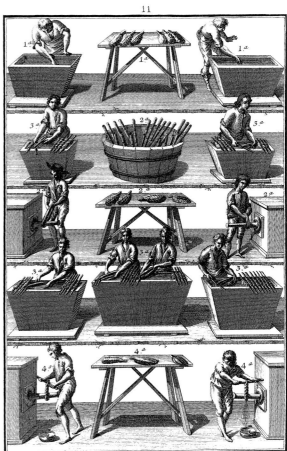

Pictures from Fernandez, L.: Arte de la tintura, *Madrid, 1778.*

Person Register

A

Abbas the Great, 129
Alexander the Great, 21, 110
Amasis, 32
Amman, Jost, 105
Aspasia, 23
Asplund, David, 105
Attila, 97
Augustus, 25
Aurelius, Marcus, 57, 58

B

Bancroft, Edward, 63, 71
Batuta, Ibn, 87
Beckmann, John, 52, 57, 61
Beda Venerabilis, 32, 33
Berntsson, Sonny, 88, 91
Berthollet, Claude Louis, 53, 108
Berzelius, Jacob, 68
Black, David, 71
Blumer, Conrad, 154
Blumer, Peter, 150
Boyle, Robert, 53
Bühler, Alfred, 131

C

Carleson, Edvard, 105
Christophersen, 190
Cicero, 77
Claudius, 77
Colbert, Jean-Baptiste, 53
Cole, William, 31, 32
Cornelius Nepos, 25, 26
Cortéz, Hernán, 49

D

d'Haristoy, 103
Dale, David, 104
Defoe, Daniel, 135
Diocletian, Gajus Aurelius Valerius, 37
Dioscorides, 58, 77
Dollfuss, H, 144
Donkin, R.A., 48
Drebbel, Cornelius, 52

E

Ekroth-Edebo, Margareta, 76

F

Fatima, 158
Fazy, 136
Flachat, 103
Flavius Vopiscus, 57
Franco Sacchetti, 63
Fraquet, 103
Friedländer, Paul, 20, 188

G

Gager, Thomas, 46
Goethe, Johann Wolfgang von, 188
Gouhard, 103

H

Hellot, 178
Hermbstedt, Friedreich, 109,123
Herodotus, 32, 77, 110
Hesekiel, 17
Hiram, 24
Huet, Jean-Baptiste, 136

J

Jenny, family, 150

K

Kang-Hsis, 49
Karl the Great, 80
Kipling, Rudyard, 122
Koechlin, Daniel, 144
Koechlin, Samuel, 144
Kralj, Niko, 13
Kuffelar, 53

L

Landivar, R, 47
Lidbeck, Gustaf, 80
Linder, Johan, 75
Linné, Carl von, 51

Index

OEUVRES
DE
MR MARIOTTE,
de l' Académie Royale des Sciences;
DIVISÉES EN DEUX TOMES,
Comprenant tous les Traitez de cet Auteur,
tant ceux qui avoient déja paru séparément,
que ceux qui n'avoient pas encore été publiez;

Imprimées sur les Exemplaires les plus exacts & les plus complets;
Revuës & corrigées de nouveau.

TOME PREMIER.

A LEIDE,
Chez PIERRE VANDER Aa,
Marchand Libraire, Imprimeur de l'Université & de la Ville.

M D C C XVII.

Thanks

A work of technical literature is often the result of many people working together, and this is true with this book. For that reason I owe warm thanks to a great number of people and institutions for their assistance, support and encouragement while writing.

Primarily my friend Jan Sisefsky, for critical review of the manuscript as a whole, but also for designing the book's section on chemistry.

Librarian Marianne Berggren for valuable review of the manuscript while the work was in progress.

Librarian Margreta Bond-Fahlberg, for covering scientific reports and documents of great value to this work.

Margareta Ekroth-Edebo, Stiftelsen Västsvensk Konservatorsateljé (Western Swedish Foundation Curator Studio), Göteborg, for dyestuff analysis of textile materials that were presented in this book.

Olle and Elisabeth Sandberg for many years of translating technical literature and reports.

Kristina Sandberg-Wadensten, Alingsås Museum, for cataloging work on the collected textile material.

Rector Mikael Hirsch, for procuring and translating Hebrew texts from the old testament.

Textile researcher Sonny Berntsson for collecting textile materials and literary assistance in the section on Anatolian folk art.

Antiquarian Märta Lindström, Lund, and the textile designer Lena Ringensson, Borås, for their participation in various documentation trips to the mountain towns of Macedonia.

To my Swiss friend Toni Strolz, Wetzikon, for his many years of contributions of various sorts for the latter part of this book, I offer especially warm thanks.

The same is also true of Dr. Heinz Kindlimann and his wife Schwanden, who generously placed invaluable archival materials regarding the various stages of calico production at my disposal.

A number of institutions and their employees have also given me a
great deal of help, and I wish to make special mention of the following:
Curator Monique Dorsson, Musée de l'Impression sur Etoffes, Mulhouse.

Associate Professor Margareta Nockert, Riksantikvarieämbetet
([Swedish] Central Board of National Antiques, Stockholm).

Assistant librarian Anders Warén, National Museum of Natural History, Stockholm.
Curator Gunilla Amnehäll, Ethnographic Museum, Göteborg.

Curator Birgitta Dandanell, Dalarnas Museum, Falun.
I wish to give special thanks to curator Inga Wintzell, Stockholm,
for both manuscript reading and for a friendly
"Picture of the Author."

Important and warm thanks to my friends
and supporters who have participated in work symposiums about red textiles
at Sätergläntans Kursgård in Dalarna.

Sweden's authors foundation
and Carl Kempes Foundation provided grants
that made completion of this book possible. I thank them warmly for this.

I will also convey warm thanks to Berit Wallenberg's Foundation which offered a generous
contribution for printing of the color photos in this book.

To designer Lena Nessle and publishing editor Eva-Maria Westberg
who both with feeling, sensitivity, and skill shaped my
thoughts, photos, and manuscript texts into a harmonious and beautiful work,
I offer sincere and warm thanks.

To my wife Gunnel, who participated in trips for this book
and in the discussions that accompanied every phase in its production,
I give the warmest of all my thanks.

Gösta Sandberg